P9-APA-507

UNIVERSITY OF WINNIPEG
DISCARDED
515 Portage Avenue
Winnipeg, Manitoba R3B 2E9

A Trip into the Blue

and other stories from
The New Yorker

Also by Richard Berczeller

DISPLACED DOCTOR
TIME WAS

PS
3552
·E593T7
1980

A Trip into the Blue

and other stories from
The New Yorker

RICHARD BERCZELLER

A&W PUBLISHERS, INC.
NEW YORK

Copyright © 1963, 1964, 1965, 1966, 1970, 1972, 1974, 1980 by Richard Berczeller

All rights reserved. No part of this work may be reproduced or transmitted in any form or by any means, electronic or mechanical, including photocopying, recording, or any information storage and retrieval system, without permission in writing from the publisher.

Published by
A & W Publishers, Inc.
95 Madison Avenue
New York, New York 10016

BOOK DESIGN: RONALD F. SHEY

Library of Congress Cataloging in Publication Data

Berczeller, Richard.
    A trip into the blue, and other stories from the New Yorker.

    CONTENTS: A trip into the blue.—The revanche.—Sodom and Gomorrah. [etc.]
    I. Title.
PZ4.B4884Tr   [PS3552.E693]   813'.54   79-26955
ISBN 0-89479-066-8

THESE STORIES ORIGINALLY APPEARED IN *The New Yorker* MAGAZINE.

Printed in the United States of America

TO MY GRANDCHILDREN PAUL AND JOHN

"WHAT A LONG WAY MANKIND HAD TO GO UNTIL ARRIVING TO A POINT TO BE MILD TO THE GUILTY . . ."

JOHANN WOLFGANG VON GOETHE

Contents

A Trip into the Blue

WE were sitting at a little round table outside the Café Marignan on the Champs-Elysées, drinking white wine. The German armies were approaching Paris— it was 1940—and the best apéritifs had gone underground. My companions were Bruno and Otto, two brothers, refugees, like me, from Austria—they from Eisenstadt, I from Mattersburg, twelve miles away, where I had been a country doctor. Now I was living as best I could in Paris, which would not issue medical licenses to refugees. I had run into them one day. Otto was selling tickets for the Loterie Nationale; Bruno was working in a shooting gallery. We had known each other back in Eisenstadt. The *"feschen Brüder,"* they were called—the dashing brothers—because of their jet-black eyes and strikingly handsome appearance. Through that spring, we would meet every Sunday and

1

talk of home. The warmth of the spring afternoons, the lazy shuffle of the passersby, the sense of danger, all were reminiscent of pre-Anschluss Vienna, and we talked and talked.

Of course, we got around to the *Reisen ins Blaue*, the trips into the blue. These had been the rage of Vienna for a brief time in the early thirties—a scheme cooked up during the depression by the near-bankrupt Austrian railroads to stimulate passenger traffic. They were Sunday excursions, departing from the Western Railroad Station in Vienna. One bought a ticket not knowing the destination or the entertainment to be provided, and a day of delight and surprise unfolded. People came from as far as Bischofshofen, three hundred miles away, just to take the ride. The brothers and I, it seemed, had all taken a trip into the blue.

Tickets were hard to come by, and I still recall the excitement I felt when I managed to obtain a pair. On a clear June morning, Mutzi, my fiancée, and I showed up at the station and fought our way through the crowd waiting for cancellations, which rarely came. Mutzi was dressed in a blue cotton dress and red shoes; her ribboned hair swung at her shoulders in nervous arcs as departure time approached. On the train, we found standing room in the corridor. The locomotive whistle tooted. The conductor entered the carriage, officious and self-important; with a flourish, he pulled down the blinds. We passengers knew we must not ask where we were going—the whole point of the trip into the blue was the surprise ending. The train got under way, and we chatted expectantly, trying to guess our direction from the lurches and motions. We could easily have pulled up the blinds and peeked out, but that would not have been fair; besides, it would have spoiled the excitement.

After an hour, the train stopped. Outside, we could

hear the blaring of a band, the sound of a large crowd; the conductor rushed in and raised the blinds, and we looked out. We were at Melk an der Donau! We didn't know where to look first. On the station platform, a fifty-piece band in scarlet uniforms was playing a Strauss waltz. Around the band milled over a thousand townspeople dressed in their Sunday best. On the mountaintop overlooking the station loomed the Stift von Melk, the world-famous twin-towered cloisters. Below—easily twenty-five hundred feet below—the waters of the Danube glittered. Before we could catch our breath, we were hustled out of the train, and the round of festivities began: lunch on the lawn under a striped awning at the Gasthaus zu den Drei Schwarzen Katzen, the band still playing; dancing on the great platform; a trip in a horse-drawn carriage to the castle; a speech by the Bürgermeister; a serenade by the children's choir of the abbey; dinner in the cellar of the Stift; more dancing and singing. Exhilarated, I had leaped to the top of a table to lead the singing:

> "*Wien, Wien, nur Du allein,*
> *Sollst stets die Stadt meiner Träume sein . . .*"
> ("Vienna, Vienna, only you,
> You are the city of my dreams . . .")

It was past midnight when we were reluctantly shepherded back to the train—exhausted, happy, and fulfilled.

I described it all to Bruno and Otto.

"Trips into the blue, pfah!" Bruno said. "They were a disgrace, a phony."

Otto agreed.

"Why do you say that?" I protested. "I had a wonderful time!"

Bruno swallowed his wine. "They were a swindle. Only the gullible could fall for it. We had a terrible time."

It took some prying to get the story, but I got it finally. Otto and Bruno had saved their money for over six months for a trip into the blue. They were the talk of the old ghetto in Eisenstadt as they left one Saturday afternoon, dressed in new black suits and white silk shirts, for the forty-mile ride to Vienna. They were taking no chance of being late and had left a day early; they spent the night sleeping on benches in the Vienna railroad station. On Sunday morning, they boarded the train; the blinds were pulled down; the departure was on time. An hour and a half later, they heard the sounds of a band; the blinds were pulled up, and they looked out. They were in Eisenstadt!

Their mortification was not to be private. On the platform was the usual crowd, and in the crowd were their friends, who were not slow in spotting them. Of course, the word spread rapidly all over town; Otto and Bruno became the center of a great wave of hilarity. They heard the mayor welcome the visitors to the home of Haydn, and then depart from his prepared text to say a special word to those who were returning to get a fresh view of their own home town. They revisited the ancient baroque château of the Esterházy princes, where in the *Musiksaal* the Haydn piano still stood; they followed the crowd to the grave of the Maestro in the Bergkirche, which they had seen many times before. They ate at the now crowded Hotel zur Weissen Rose; on any ordinary Sunday, they could quietly and happily drink the afternoon away there. A stone's throw from the château stood the old ghetto where the brothers lived: dozens of narrow buildings that mirrored the changing architecture of the centuries—a courtyard with Renaissance arches and Gothic columns, a medieval synagogue, Renaissance doors with baroque locks. The crushing blow came when the guides led the group to the brothers' own house to call attention to a baroque angel over the doorway and a particularly fine gargoyle perched above the second-story eaves.

It was at this point that their old *Mutter* came out to look at the crowd. She saw her sons standing there, red-faced. Her astonishment turned to glee, and she sang out, loud enough to be heard by everyone, "You see, Bruno, Otto, there is no place like your own home. That's what I have always said, and now you can see for yourself."

The brothers were entitled to the return trip to Vienna, but they didn't take it.

———

AFTER the Germans entered Paris, I managed to get to the United States. The last word I had of Otto and Bruno was that they were in a labor camp at Montauban, in the South of France. There was much for me to do trying to get adjusted to a new life in New York, and the brothers slipped from my mind.

One day, I was seeing patients in the clinic at Beth Israel Hospital. It was a year after the end of the war. A new group of refugees had just arrived in New York, and my job was examinations and general health screening. An emaciated old man spoke to me. "You're Dr. Berczeller, aren't you?"

"Why, yes," I said. I didn't recognize him.

"From Mattersburg?"

"Yes."

He had been a haberdasher in Eisenstadt. Although we hadn't known each other, we found we had a number of friends in common, and we talked about them. Inevitably, I got around to asking for Bruno and Otto, the *feschen Brüder* —had he seen them?

He had. He was in the labor camp with them at Montauban. He even knew what had happened to them. One day, he saw them herded into a freight car headed for Auschwitz. As the S.S. troops lowered the sliding panels to lock them in, he heard Bruno say to Otto, "Well, another trip into the blue."

The Revanche

BEFORE the First World War, Sopron-Ödenburg was one of the largest garrison cities of the Austro-Hungarian Empire. It was an élite garrison. Barons, counts, dukes, and occasionally an archduke strolled with fellow-officers on Sunday mornings along the main boulevard (now renamed Lenin Körút). In the sky-blue, green-and-scarlet-braided tunics of their respective regiments, and with clinking spurs and mighty sabres, they were much admired by the burghers, and especially by the ladies. Sunday afternoons were given over to privates and noncommissioned officers, who promenaded with maids from households in every corner of the city.

The military was a fluctuating element in a society that had remained unchanged for centuries. Sopron-Ödenburg went back to the time of the Romans. During the Middle

7

Ages, it was a fortified frontier town, and for a few years even a royal residence. Most of the burghers could trace their histories back to the medieval guilds, and any family whose tree stopped short of two hundred years was likely to be regarded as foreign. Nevertheless, the soldiers were an accepted part of the city's life. Indeed, it was conditioned by them. When taps sounded from the Army barracks, the burghers retired, and when a trumpet signalled that a platoon was on its way to the exercise grounds they awoke. Merchants depended on the soldiers' pay for their business (although privates earned as little as three cents a day), and at night the officers bought champagne for the chorus girls of the city theatre.

It was an exciting atmosphere for a boy to grow up in. By the age of seven, I was imbued with the prevailing spirit of patriotism and knew the ranks from corporal to lieutenant general almost before I could spell simple words. We boys were in constant attendance at the exercise grounds and often marched behind the brass band.

My Uncle Solomon, himself a former sergeant with the Hussars, gave me an additional education in military matters. He was the only Jewish baker in town—a seventh-generation baker, he liked to say, for the Jewish population in Sopron-Ödenburg, too, had antecedents dating back many centuries. When I was eight, I used to rush to the bakery in the Kirchengasse every day after school. I was Uncle Solomon's favorite nephew—his wife, Hannah, was my mother's cousin—and I had been elected to wake him from his afternoon nap. I would find him slumped in a chair, his large bald head resting on a table. While he slept, giant logs burned in the oven, heating it to the right temperature for baking. At precisely three o'clock, when I heard the bell of the Evangelical Church nearby, I would touch him on the shoulder. He would look at me with one eye, stretch, rise, and lift me high in the air, my stomach tingling. "You're a good boy," he would say, easing me back to earth. Then he commanded me to stand straight and he himself came to attention. "*Habt acht!*" he would shout. "Chin up! Chest out! Stomach in! That's the boy." He stepped smartly to the oven while I followed at a march.

After this ritual, he went about the business of baking. Descending into a shallow pit, he took up a mammoth poker and hammered the glimmering logs into ash. This he brushed from the oven, replacing it with pale, lifeless dough, thrust deep inside on a paddle. As he worked, pearls of perspiration collected on his bristling red mustache. I liked to watch the dough turn pink and brown and become transformed into the familiar bread and rolls sold out in the front of the store. Customers came from everywhere—even Kapuvár, thirty kilometres away—Jews and Gentiles alike. Aunt Hannah did the selling, while Uncle sat behind the counter writing tiny Hebrew characters in his account book. Peasants paid only once a year, at harvest time.

I still remember every corner of that mysterious realm: the dark, deep doorway, the narrow winding stairs leading up to the living quarters, the dormitory where the six baker's helpers lived and slept, three at a time, while the others worked their twelve-hour shift. I spent hours there, watching Uncle at work and listening to his stories. They were mostly about his younger years. After an apprenticeship with his father, he had been dispatched to Vienna to learn how to make fancy pastry. He told me about his evenings at the Theater an der Wien, where he listened to Strauss and Lehár operettas. He could whistle all the principal themes. And when he recounted his visits to the Hofburg-theater, he would stand before the oven, lift one arm dramatically, and recite Schiller, Goethe, and Shakespeare. Probably the most exciting tales of all were drawn from his

Wanderjahre through Germany. Like most Jews of his generation, he was enthusiastically pro-German. "Richard," he would say, "one day you must see it with your own eyes —München, Hamburg, and Berlin! The tremendous traffic, the crowds of people, the Untergrundbahn that takes you in a couple of minutes from one part of the city to another." And I never tired of hearing about the parade he had witnessed on the Potsdamer Platz, where the Kaiser stood on a platform reviewing his troops. "Infantry, Richard! Cavalry! Cannon as big as our city tower!"

And sometimes Uncle would tell me about his three years in service with the Hussars. He was the best marksman in the whole 9th Regiment, and he had a medal to prove it. It still adorned his tunic, which hung in a closet, and though I had seen it many times, I was never permitted to touch it. "*Ja*, Richard," he often said, "those were great times. Then a soldier was a real soldier. We took the oath to defend His Majesty and our country, and we meant it. But how the world has changed. . . ."

My father often warned me to keep away from Uncle's establishment: it was unventilated and filthy.

"But I get sugar-coated horns," I said.

That was precisely what he didn't like. And he had no use for Uncle Solomon. "That *Dummkopf!*" he called him.

I was torn in my loyalty between the two men. I loved them both, and I wished that they might be friends. They never were. There were hardly two people more unalike.

Father came to Sopron-Ödenburg from northern Hungary (now Czechoslovakia) when he was nineteen. He was the black sheep in an upper-middle-class family. One of his uncles was a surgeon general, and another a famous gynecologist and director of the Jewish Hospital in Budapest. The family name derived from the name of the town. Father became interested in politics while he was still in the *Gymnasium*. He was dismissed from school after distribut-

ing anti-government leaflets, and subsequently he ran away
to Budapest, where he became a printer's apprentice. Soon
he was involved in the trade-union movement and was sent
to Sopron-Ödenburg, where a modern industry had just
started. He began organizing workers—first a small steel
plant, then a button factory, then a coal mine, and eventually the workers in small shops, Uncle's bakery included.
He must have had a hard time, a "foreigner" in our arch-
conservative city, and in those early days visits of the police
to the house of "the anarchist and Socialist" were frequent.
But by the time I was conscious of the world around me,
Father had established himself. He was head of the union
council and the workers' social-security panel, which main-
tained out-patient clinics for sick workingmen and their
families. We lived in a house owned by the panel. It was
the former mansion of a count—a seventeenth-century baroque building. Our living quarters were on the second
floor—tremendous rooms, with walls so thick they could
have withstood an assault from the whole garrison. From
our windows, there was a view across a courtyard to the
clinics, where posters above the entrances read, "THE
THINKING WORKER DOES NOT DRINK—THE DRINKING WORKER
DOES NOT THINK!" and "DO NOT SPIT IN THE OPEN AIR—
TUBERCULOSIS IS MURDERER NO. 1."

I have a photograph of Father dating from that period.
He is the central figure in a group of determined-looking
men wearing large cravats. He has an ample crop of hair
and side whiskers, but only the beginnings of a mustache.
He used to be embarrassed by his youthful appearance,
Mother told me. But even then his voice was strong. I often
listened outside the door when he spoke at union meetings.
These were held in a room next to our apartment, the
former state hall. Handsome old crystal chandeliers hung
from the ceiling, but the light came from sober, unshaded
electric bulbs. I would hear words like "exploitation" and

"class struggle," followed by applause. Once, I asked Father to explain the meanings of these words.

"Well," he said, "you're old enough, and I suppose you should know a few things. It's like this, Richard. There are wealthy people, and there are poor people. And we must find ways to give everybody his share—enough to eat, a decent place to live in, healthy working conditions. Not like the filth those baker's helpers live in—a dozen men stuffed into one little room."

"There are only six," I protested.

"Well, six, seven, whatever—it's bad enough."

I should have known that Father would implicate Uncle's bakery, and many months passed before I again showed any curiosity about his work.

One of my earliest recollections is of a local election campaign. It was for a municipal councilmanship, and Father was the workers' candidate—a hopeless prospect in a Protestant district inhabited mostly by well-to-do wine-growers. A poll tax prevented the majority of the workers from casting votes. Father's opponent was the scion of an old, wealthy Protestant family. Most of the Jews—themselves well-to-do citizens—were for Father's opponent, and Uncle was no exception. He would not speak openly, but one day he read me an article from a local anti-Semitic weekly directed against Father's candidacy. Some of the charges were so clearly directed at all Jews that I thought Uncle would now be forced to come to Father's defense. I waited while he folded up the paper and wiped his silver-rimmed spectacles.

"I still recall, Richard, when Jews could not vote—and now some would like to run the whole show. It does not do us any good!" He wagged a finger at the newspaper. "Jews should think twice before running for a public office. We are equal before God, yes, but there are limits. It is bad enough to try to push into office, but to be against the government *besides!*"

That night, I refused to eat. When Father came in, he observed me for a while, looked into my throat, and took my temperature. Obviously, I was in sound health. What was wrong, he asked me.

"Nothing," I mumbled.

He shrugged and settled down to his dinner. He and Mother discussed the campaign. Then he turned to me again. "What is it? Troubles in school?"

"No," I blurted, "it's you—Jews should not run for office—"

"What!" He half rose from his chair, as though to strike me. "Who told you that?" he shouted. "That old *Dummkopf.*"

"Please," my mother said.

He turned on her. "It's also your fault. You should watch where the boy spends his time."

I cried, Mother cried, and the episode ended with Father's order that I must never again go to the bakery.

I felt guilty for having betrayed Uncle's feelings, and I was prepared to stay away for a while. In any event, there was much to keep me occupied at home. The election campaign was growing more intense. Anonymous letters threatened Father's life, and he was accompanied everywhere by bodyguards—two stern, heavily mustachioed coal miners. At night, the entrance to our apartment was barricaded, and we lived as though in a fortress. This was exciting, and I could not help feeling pleased when I heard that Father was beginning to win over new support. The campaign meetings moved from the back room of a little inn into the open air. Finally, the day came. Father was elected by a tiny majority. The crucial vote came from the winegrowers, whom Father had persuaded to vote along with the workers, on the ground that they were workers also. Besides, there had been a dip in prices on the wine market; the winegrowers were ready to risk a change.

That night, there was a great victory celebration in our courtyard, which was jammed with people holding torches aloft. They sang one song over and over:

"Brüder zur Sonne, zur Freiheit,
Brüder zum Lichte empor."

AFTER the election, our household returned to normal, and I began to think wistfully of the bakery. Father was busy with his new political role and seemed to take no notice of me. My circles around the bakery grew smaller and smaller, and finally one day I woke Uncle from his afternoon nap at the appointed time. He gave no sign of noticing that I had been away. He commanded me to stand at attention, and I obeyed with a snap. In a minute, we were comrades again.

On Tuesdays, the Sunday edition of the Vienna *Neue Freie Presse* arrived, and Uncle would read aloud the exciting news from the Balkan Peninsula—Bulgaria, Turkey, Greece—and Serbia and Montenegro, those two allies of Russia and the potential enemies of Austria. "We shouldn't wait!" he thundered. "A preventive war could crush those midgets like lice!"

"And what would Russia say?" I asked, for I was becoming quite knowledgeable about the international scene.

"Ha, ha—that giant with clay feet," he said.

"And France?"

"She wouldn't dare interfere. One day, you'll learn about her defeat at Sedan by the great Bismarck—and as for the British, the German U-boats would soon take care of her navy."

At home, when Father and the sombre shop stewards met, I listened to another version. When the warmongers in Vienna, St. Petersburg, and other capitals unleashed a general war, the workers would strike. The international labor movement would stop that nonsense even before it started. They believed in the popular labor slogan "All wheels would stand still, if only your strong arm wills it."

Each time Aunt Hannah found her husband reading to me from the *Neue Freie Presse*, she sounded her warning "Solomon!" Uncle did not argue with his wife. She was a tiny, thin woman with large, pitch-black eyes, and always on the run. In the morning, she counted the rolls into delivery baskets, talked to customers about their problems, scurried upstairs to put the apartment in order, and returned to supervise the helpers. Much of the afternoon she spent mending the laundry. And still she found time to meet my mother a half-dozen times a day.

The two women were not only relatives but friends, and the aversion their husbands had for each other did not disturb their mutual affection. They tried hard to establish a token relationship between our families, and I recall a few times when we were visited by Uncle Solomon and Aunt Hannah or when we called on them. The two men would sit stiffly and address each other in the most constrained manner. On one occasion, shortly after Father had begun to organize the workers of smaller shops, Uncle spoke about the destruction of the paternal relationship between the worker and his master.

"But aren't you a worker?" my father said.

"What do you mean!" Uncle snapped.

"You work fourteen hours a day. You hardly find time to relax. That makes you a worker, doesn't it?"

"I am a *Bürger*," Uncle said haughtily. "I pay taxes. I have nothing to do with workers."

A chilly silence fell on everyone.

Then something happened that severed our family relations. Uncle liked to tell me ghost stories and recount his dreams, which he took very seriously. Although both his parents had been dead for many years, he would consult with them about business matters. One day, he seemed depressed. I watched him while he stirred the logs in the oven, and then I asked him what was wrong.

He put his poker aside. "Last night," he said quietly, "I had a long talk with Mother. She wore her black kerchief with the white fringe—the one she wore only on the high holy days. 'Solomon,' she said, 'I'm lonesome for you. Aren't you my favorite son? You must join me.' I said it was impossible—who would care for the bakery? But she only shook her head. 'Tomorrow at noon,' she said. 'I'll be waiting for you.' Then she disappeared."

I felt my throat tightening. "But it was just a dream," I said.

"Mother was a strong-willed woman," Uncle said with finality, and went back to look after the oven.

As soon as I left him, I searched for Aunt. I found her scrubbing a floor upstairs. "Poor Uncle!" I cried. In a quavering voice, I told her about his dream, and when I finished she burst out laughing. I felt foolish. Nevertheless, I could not rid myself of the presentiment that Uncle was going to die, and I thought of nothing else until bedtime.

The next day at school, I feigned illness, and the teacher excused me. I hurried to the bakery. In the oven, the logs had been neatly arranged, ready to be lighted by Uncle at noon. I crept up the stairs and into his room. He was sleeping peacefully, the billowing quilts above him moving gently up and down. His nightcap was tilted over one eye. I settled down beside the bed and watched him, waiting for the church bell.

On the last stroke, Aunt Hannah appeared at the threshold. She did not see me. "Solomon!" she called. "It's time to light the oven. Your mother must have changed her mind."

I jumped to my feet.

"What are you doing here?" she said. "You should be in school. Go back immediately!"

Uncle opened his eyes, stretched, and sat up. His eyes caught mine. "Go back to school," he said sheepishly.

I went to a park nearby and spent the afternoon wandering aimlessly and throwing stones into water puddles. There were no children around, and it was a boring day. When I arrived home, I found Mother in a frantic state. She had been notified by the teacher of my "illness" and thought I might be lying half dead in an alley. I couldn't be found anywhere. In spite of my explanation, I got a sound thrashing, and that was not the end of it. She reported everything to Father—something she had never done before when I had misbehaved.

He flew into a rage. "Everywhere my word means something but at home!" he shouted. "How many times have I told the boy to keep away from that place! He has been frightened by that *Dummkopf!*"

I began to cry. "But Uncle did not die," I said. "I didn't want him to die, and he didn't."

"That's what I mean," Father said. "He frightened you. It's stupid and cruel."

I expected to be punished, and was surprised when Father told me to sit down and sat beside me. "Listen, Richard," he said calmly. "Uncle told you a story, and I'm sure he has told you similar stories. I don't want you ever to listen to such talk. You must never—I mean *never*—go back to him again."

In the beginning, I felt bad—as though Uncle Solomon really had died. But gradually Father replaced him as my mentor. On Sunday mornings, we walked through the woods in the foothills of the Alps. We collected cyclamen, which, in the shade of the mammoth fir trees, grew very large. And Father, who was raised in forest country, taught me to distinguish between edible and poisonous mushrooms. I listened with greater interest than before to his stories about the out-patient clinics. In simple terms, he explained the theory of preventive medicine to me. He was a very articulate man, and I began to acquire a rudimentary grasp of his ideas. More important, I felt that I was sharing what lay closest to his heart. In military matters, however, we remained irreconcilable. "Why do we need all those soldiers?" Father said repeatedly. "It must lead to a war."

"But we'd beat them, wouldn't we?" I always answered enthusiastically.

This sort of talk seemed purely theoretical. We lived in an aura of peace. The stores were crammed with merchandise. The coffeehouses prospered. The officers were more elegant than ever, and their parties were big social events. They were held in the garden of the country club, which, for the day, was enclosed within a high board fence painted green. The burghers, excluded from the spectacle inside, would prance up and down on the sidewalk. We boys, naturally, scaled the fence and spied on the glittering guests below—the officers in their best uniforms, and their ladies in dresses with deep décolletage, the mayor, the big industrialists, and a few city councilmen.

In the spring of 1914, Uncle fell ill. For the first time in two years, Aunt Hannah came to our house. She cried as she described how she had found him lying on the floor before the oven. (He must have had a coronary, which at that period could not be diagnosed.) His condition was so serious that we could not visit him for three weeks. I accompanied my parents and was much shaken when I saw him. He had aged, and his face had become thin and as pale as dough. He must have seen my concern, for when I bent over him he embraced me warmly and assured me that he would soon be well.

From that day on, I visited his bedside daily and read aloud to him from the *Presse*. Father did not object. I was present when Uncle took his first steps, and a week later I supported him down the stairs. Much of his work had been taken over by his helpers, and he returned to bed each afternoon for his nap, where I would waken him, as formerly, at three o'clock sharp. Little by little, he resumed his old routine.

One sunny afternoon in June, I was strolling with friends in the Elisabeth-park, where twice weekly a military band gave concerts. I still recall that they were playing a tune from "The Gypsy Baron" when someone ran up to the conductor and whispered in his ear. He stopped the music in the middle of a phrase and turned to the audience, his mouth quivering. "Erzherzog Franz Ferdinand and his consort have been murdered . . . in Sarajevo," he announced. The chatting around the kiosk ceased instantly. The crowd began to disperse quickly.

Immediately, I hurried to the bakery. Despite the gauntness of his face, Uncle's eyes had the old gleam. "Didn't I tell you, Richard? The shots may have been fired in Sarajevo, but the trigger was pulled in Belgrade and St. Petersburg. How long will our patience last!"

It did not last long. On the twenty-eighth of July, Austria declared war on Serbia. Russia, Germany, France, and Britain entered the conflict. When Germany entered the war, Uncle hung a picture of Kaiser Wilhelm on the wall, stood at attention, and sang:

"Es braust ein Ruf wie Donnerhall,
Wie Schwertgeklirr und Wogenprall,
Am Rhein, am Rhein, am Deutschen Rhein."

The war had unanimous support in those days. In gray uniforms, the shop stewards marched together with the burghers to the rail station, while the population strewed flowers before them. Father was one of the soldiers, and the night before he left Uncle came to wish him well. He shook Father's hand and said something heartening about being home by harvest time.

Father looked very smart in his uniform, decorated with the stars of an artillery sergeant, but he had little to say. At the rail station, when he looked down on us from his compartment window, his eyes were sad.

Uncle bought a large map of Europe and nailed it to the table. The *Neue Freie Presse*, though two days late, arrived daily, and after reading the bulletins he stuck little flags on his map to delineate the front lines. Things did not go as well as expected in Serbia. After an initial thrust, our armies were stopped. "Don't worry," Uncle reassured me. "I know that territory like my own palms. Right at that spot we often stopped in our maneuvers to get fresh supplies and Army reserves. We are playing a cat-and-mouse game with the Serbians, and soon the jaws will close on the mouse—like that!"

From Russia, our armies cut into Polish territory. Uncle said, "Soon we'll be in Warsaw, and from there it's only a short hop to St. Petersburg. *Der böse Mann* there will soon find out that it was easier to kill helpless Jews in his pogroms than to fight a real war."

I was deeply convinced of the justness of our cause and was only sorry that at thirteen I was not old enough to be on the battlefield.

At home, the atmosphere changed. The pink, censored postcards from Father, who was on the Russian front, arrived only sporadically, and I was often wakened at night by Mother's sobbing. During the first winter of the war, our dark castle apartment was freezing cold, and from all around came bad news. Our neighbor, a cobbler, was killed in action, leaving a wife and eight children. My two first cousins, a few years older than I, were both killed in Russia. Under the heading "Died in Action on the Field of Honor," lengthy lists appeared daily in the papers. Nearly everything was rationed. The shortage of fuel and bread struck hardest of all. Long lines waited in front of bakeries.

We could not have managed without help from Uncle and Aunt. Uncle's oven was lighted only three times a week—sometimes only twice. Grain arrived after much delay. There were no rolls, and the bread grew darker and darker. Uncle stood behind the counter to cut the bread into slices and weigh them, and the rations grew smaller. Often those at the end of the line, waiting since dawn, had to be turned away. Aunt would come to us after dark with a few pieces of bread hidden in her satchel.

Uncle remained optimistic. Since his baking was curtailed, he had more time to follow the war. The Russian forces had penetrated into Austrian territory but were beaten, and retreated, leaving hundreds of thousands of war prisoners behind. In their dirty-green coats, they marched through our town on their way to camps. The Russian thrust into East Prussia was also turned back. Uncle was jubilant. "Didn't I tell you?" he said to me. "Hindenburg, the greatest *Feldherr* in history, lured them to the Masurian Marshes, and there they perished by the millions. . . ."

When the Italians entered the war, he was furious. "Those dirty cowards!" he shouted. "In 1859, they stole Lombardy from us, and now they stab us in the back. They'll pay dearly!"

And, of course, he waited impatiently for the fall of Paris.

———————◆———————

My first doubts began in December, 1916, when Father arrived home on leave. He came from the Italian front, where he had been transferred from Russia. He looked well, his face ruddy, his hair graying at the temples. He wore many medals, and I walked proudly at his side on the boulevard. Numbers of people visited us, Uncle among them. He looked with admiration at Father, and said how sorry he was that age prevented him from joining the heroic troops on the battlefield. "Soon we'll be in Rome," he said, smiling.

Father looked at him squarely. "At present we're bogged down on the Doberdo Plateau and the Isonzo River," he said. "The war will end before we get to Rome."

"But only in victory!" said Uncle.

"For whom?" Father asked quietly.

Uncle looked to me as if asking for support, then he shrugged his shoulders. "A soldier should never speak that way," he said in a whisper. He got up and left.

Our armies now occupied large areas of enemy territory. Why shouldn't we win the war, I asked Father as we walked through the woods one day. His leave had lasted three weeks, and much of the time had been spent with me. I was only fifteen, but he treated me as an adult.

"What does it matter who wins?" he answered. "Are our interests different from the workers' of Russia, France, Germany, Italy? The only losers should be those who started this . . . this monstrous thing."

In the darkened assembly room, he met with shop stewards on leave and those too old to be drafted, and they talked endlessly about war and peace, about the hunger and misery of women and children in the hinterland, about widows and orphans, about the incompetence and greed of those in high office—those dark-souled men in Vienna. Finally, the day came for Father to depart. I felt saddened in a way I had not when he first went off to war.

The situation at home became graver by the day. Uncle's bakery was as cold as a cave, and for lack of fuel and grain the oven remained unlit for weeks at a time. On one occasion, the bakery was stormed by a horde of people, but they left when they found no bread.

The war flourished. Uncle was triumphant when, after the second phase of the Russian Revolution, the Bolsheviks asked for peace and we occupied Poland and the Ukraine. Then America entered the war. "What do those cowboys know about war?" he said disdainfully.

At the beginning of the year 1918, the desire for peace among the populace at home had become dangerously intense. There was a strike in a munitions factory not far from our city, and night after night one could hear detonations of gunpowder. Also, there were epidemics of typhus, caused by lice in the prisoner-of-war camps, a brief flareup of cholera, and the first cases of Spanish influenza, which, during the following two years, would take a horrible toll of the population, weakened by malnutrition. Illegal peace committees sprang up everywhere. I joined one.

During those feverish months, I did not visit Uncle for weeks at a time, but when I did I would find him sitting at the table staring at the map. I could no longer stand to hear him speak of victory. "Don't you see, Uncle Solomon," I said, "that the war is lost?"

He looked at me, bewildered. Then he shook his head. "We both speak German," he said, "but we don't understand each other anymore."

———————

By the thirty-first of October, 1918, the armies of Austria-Hungary had capitulated on all fronts, and the German Army surrendered some days later. Father had arrived home the week before. For several months, we had received no news from him, and Mother feared he was dead. But then a letter arrived from him saying that he was wounded and in a hospital behind the front.

He now walked with a cane, as his right leg was badly punctured by shrapnel, but he immediately summoned his comrades. When the news of peace reached our city, the church bells tolled, and soldiers and civilians embraced each other.

Despite my own joy, I could not help worrying about Uncle Solomon, and in the midst of the celebration I went to see him. I found him at his old table. The map had been removed. He did not speak for a minute or two, and then he said, "Well, it's over."

I nodded.

"But listen, Richard," he said sadly, "you're a learned man—unlike your uncle. You know history. The day of *Revanche* must come. The German Army—our army—will march again. Don't you think so?"

I looked at the old man, his shirtsleeves too wide for his meagre arms, his tired eyes fixed on me.

"Yes, Uncle," I said, "you are right."

WITH the collapse of the old empire, Hungary had become an independent country, stripped of its traditional government. Only the working class—the unions—was organized and had strength enough, together with units of the defeated Army, to establish a semblance of authority. A regional national assembly was formed, and Father was elected its president.

A few months later, the Republic—the first democratic experiment in Hungarian history—was overthrown by a Communist government. This, in turn, was displaced by the Horthy government, the first Fascist regime in history. In August, 1919, liberals, Socialists, unionists fled to Austria. My father was among them. Shortly after, the family joined him.

I never saw Uncle again. Each year, on the high Jewish holy days, I sent him greetings, but only Aunt Hannah replied. I knew he disliked writing letters. Mother corresponded regularly with Aunt Hannah over the years. By the time I was in medical school, Uncle's health had begun to fail badly. His legs were swollen, and his breathing had become labored, Aunt Hannah reported. Still, he walked up and down the few steps to and from the bakery, where he supervised his helpers. Flour had long since become plentiful, and the oven was lit daily, as of old. With each new letter, I diagnosed the rapid deterioration of his heart. Poor Uncle, I used to think—he would never live to see the German Army march again.

He died in his sleep, in September, 1929, ten years too soon.

Sodom and Gomorrah

WHEN I entered medical school in 1920, Vienna was suffering from the aftereffects of the war. The former residential capital of an empire of sixty million people had been reduced to being the capital city of a small country of six and a half million. Deprived of its hinterland —grain-producing Hungary and the coal mines of Silesia —Vienna was a starving and freezing city in that rigorous winter of 1920-21. We students attended lectures in unheated auditoriums, and in anatomy laboratories dissected with freezing fingers. Who among my generation of Viennese doctors does not remember the breakfast that the American Quakers served at the aula of the university— large bowls of hot chocolate and thick slices of bread, given out by those white-haired ladies, always with a smile and kind words for us in their atrocious accents. Without that nourishing breakfast we would hardly have been able to start our day in school.

The ingredients for our other meals also came from America. The Jewish Joint Distribution Committee rented a dilapidated building on the Zimmermannplatz, near the boulevard that separated Vienna proper from its suburbs, and adapted it to a student cafeteria—the Mensa Academica. Hundreds of young men and women sat around unpolished tables in that giant dining room, devouring their meals. Unshaded bulbs hung from the ceiling, and the room was far from comfortable, but it was well heated and served its purpose. We spent our free time there, studying and discussing events. In a corner was a blackboard on which notices were chalked up: meetings, lost-and-found articles, part-time jobs. There one day I discovered an advertisement for a French tutor for two children. My knowledge of French was skimpy, but I was in dire need of money. (My parents lived in Baden bei Wien, a half hour's train ride from Vienna. We were refugees from Fascist Hungary, and I could not expect help from home.) I went to Hietzing, the villa suburb of the wealthy, and introduced myself to Herr and Frau Stieglbauer. Fortunately, they did not speak French at all, and I was accepted. Three times weekly for a year and a half, I taught a ten-year-old boy and his eight-year-old sister the language of Molière, and while teaching it I learned it better myself. In addition to the three schillings' tutoring fee, I received an afternoon *Jause:* coffee with *Schlagobers* and buttered rolls. I was more than sorry when in May of 1922, on arriving at the villa, I was told by the weeping Frau Stieglbauer that my services were no longer required. Her husband's business had deteriorated to such a degree that the chauffeur, the gardener, two maids, the *Kinderfräulein*, and I all lost our jobs.

What made this more regrettable was that it occurred just before summer vacation. At the Mensa, I looked in vain for another position. But then one day there was a note on the blackboard: jobs for thirty people; the Sascha Film Company was hiring extras. The only requirement was minimal training in acting, and the fee was tremendous —five schillings (one dollar) per session!

Next morning at six, I travelled by trolley car one hour to the Laaerberg, where the film company had its studios. A long line of applicants was already waiting—mostly students of theatrical schools, I learned from the talk, and I thought my chances were slim indeed. But there I was, and I settled down and read from the anatomy book I had brought with me. I read for two hours. Then we were all called into a room, obviously the office, where behind a desk a man of about thirty with a great crop of hair sat chain-smoking. With a quick wave of the hand, he indicated that we were to walk past him. He rejected one after another. Finally, I arrived at the desk and stood facing him. His squinting eyes rested on me. Five seconds passed, and five more—I was still not rejected.

"Any training in acting?" he asked me.

"Yes," I said.

"Tell me more."

"A couple of roles in Shakespeare. I also played Franz Moor in 'Die Räuber.' "

The man's eyes brightened. Franz Moor in the Schiller drama was a major role. "In what theatre?" he asked.

"In *Gymnasium*."

This was greeted by a roar of laughter. The man smiled. "How exciting!" he said. Then he turned to two men standing with him. "Too bad," he said, amused. "The fellow has a Biblical face. It reminds me of Nebuchadnezzar in a mural I saw recently."

Again there was a salvo of mocking laughter, and I felt myself grow hot with rage. I had noticed that though he spoke good German, like a Hungarian he emphasized the first syllable of each word. "Someday I hope to meet you when we are alone!" I shouted at him in Hungarian.

The man got up and walked around the desk toward me. He raised his right hand, and I was preparing for a fistfight, but he placed his hand gently on my shoulder. "We Hungarians have a terrible temper, haven't we?" he said, and laughed.

He had a terrible temper, Michael Kertész, the director for the Sascha Film Company. He shouted, screamed on all occasions. But I was one of the thirty extras. "Hurry up!" he said impatiently as he conducted us to the dressing room. There we exchanged our street clothes for white gowns. Soon we learned what they signified.

It was a sunny morning but brisk, as it is in late May in Vienna. We marched to the open-air studios (the sun was the only source of light for filmmaking in those days). Kertész, sitting high on a ladder, was yelling at the stagehands, who carried papier-mâché buildings from a warehouse. At one side stood a small group of men and women in white gowns like ours. I recognized them all: well-known actors and actresses of the legitimate theatre. At last, the stage was set, the technicians disappeared, and the cameraman came out from the office building.

"Let's begin!" Kertész shouted from his height. "Ladies and gentlemen of the cast. Our production is the Biblical drama 'Sodom and Gomorrah.'" He took a tattered book from his pocket. "This is the Book of Genesis. Should I read the chapter that deals with our subject?"

"No!" we boomed in unison. We were freezing in our Biblical costumes.

"Very well," Kertész said. "Then we shall begin." I could see that he had prepared himself for a speech.

During the next two months, the mass scenes of the movie were filmed; the sinning population of the doomed towns committed crimes against God and their fellow-men. Hour after hour, day after day, the thirty of us attacked Lot's house, only to be stopped by two corpulent angels. Kertész screamed at us, "Fools! You stroll as if you were on the Kärntner Strasse. *Attack*, you sons of bitches! Again! Again, you . . ." until he gave a sign to the cameraman, a middle-aged, dour-faced man with gypsy-black hair, to start shooting the scene. Often when we arrived in the morning, the sun hid behind clouds, and those days, with a grim face, Kertész handed us our five schillings at the gate. It was always he who paid our salaries.

Not everything I had expected when I entered the world of glamour materialized in the hysterical atmosphere, the hustle and bustle, the dreariness of the papier-mâché houses. But the five schillings reconciled me to the shortcomings of the job. My living standard improved. I bought a much needed suit and a pair of shoes. I ate better, and my mother's eyes rested on me with satisfaction. I could even help my parents and my brothers, who were still in the *Gymnasium*. Food was rationed, and low in calories. Mother obviously did not divide it evenly; when I came home for the weekends, I found her face smaller and smaller. But everything could be bought on the black market, and on my visits now I carried in my briefcase bread, meat, shortenings. Father did not know—he would have resented it bitterly.

Father was in his mid-forties. He had been a pioneer in the welfare program of the workers in western Hungary— a high official in the social-security and sick-benefit foundation—and he could not find an equal job as a refugee in

Austria. In the small positions he did find here and there, he earned too much to die but not enough to live decently. Still, he was too proud to accept support from anyone—especially from a son. He knew of my job at the Sascha Film Company, of course, but he had no interest in it; it was an emergency solution. Father was not a doctor himself, but he came from a family of doctors, and all his life medicine was the essence of his existence.

Mother, on the other hand, was curious about my new career. "Tell me more," she would say, making sure that Father was not around. Her own interests included the arts: theatre, movies, music. She had a warm, pleasant voice. Before I opened my eyes mornings, I would hear her singing as she moved about the apartment preparing breakfast, checking Father's clothes for the day. *"Leise flehen meine Lieder"*—she loved Schubert. She wanted to know everything about the picture-making, but when I had finished telling her she would always say, "Yes, it is interesting. But Richard, do not neglect your studies."

Those I neglected indeed. The hours of my lectures often conflicted with the time I spent on the Laaerberg. In anatomy lab, I was behind the others; the leg that had been assigned to me for dissection was only half done. One afternoon, the anatomy instructor warned me that if I didn't finish in time I would flunk. Next day, I asked for an interview with Kertész to request time off. As always when a subject didn't interest him, he listened with only one ear. Then he said he would try to work something out. That was the last I heard of the matter. So I explained my predicament to the instructor and arranged with him to dissect during the evening hours.

Out on the Laaerberg, Kertész was pushing those scenes that required a large personnel. The payroll with the extras weighed heavily on his meagre budget. (Often, sombre-looking strangers—the men who financed the venture—watched the shooting, while Kertész smoked more than usual.) Little by little, one extra after another was given notice, until only a few of us remained. Then, one day when I arrived for work, the doorman told me I must report immediately at Kertész' office. Walking through the anteroom, all I could think of was the blackboard at the Mensa, with its chalked-up notices of jobs. But Kertész received me cordially, offered me a seat and a cigarette. He asked me how things were going, and I thought he was even paying attention as I answered. He rose and walked up and down, taking side glances at me. He stopped in front of me. "D'you want to continue with us?" he asked.

It took a few seconds to collect myself. "I just told you," I said. "I'm behind in anatomy lab—"

"O.K.," he interrupted. "We can talk about that, too. Now, listen." He switched to Hungarian. "I've been watching you, and I want to be fair. You're no Conrad Veidt yet, but maybe something can be made of you— maybe. What I need immediately is someone to take over the part of Lot. Herr Schwendtner complains of chest pains—he's not going to be able to continue."

I protested. "But medical students are forbidden to take part in extracurricular activities. The university—"

"They needn't know. We'll use a pseudonym." Kertész narrowed his eyes. "Your fee will be *fifty* schillings a session! *Te marha.*" ("You blockhead.") He looked at me sternly.

———

I HAD a hard time. The rehearsals were agony. Kertész interrupted me steadily with abuse. "You *are* Lot, you stupid son of a bitch! The only one in those goddam towns who was selected by the Almighty! Don't you understand? Why the hell did I ever think you could do it!" Moaning, he tore at his hair. At last, still moaning, he gave the sign to the cameraman. And then we would move to the next scene, and new abuses. I often was close to pulling off my Biblical costume and walking out.

Otherwise, Kertész kept his word; he accepted the demands of medical school and allowed me time for lectures. Still, it often happened that while I was in the midst of lab work I was called out and in the corridor one of Kertész' messengers would be waiting.

In November, the filming was completed, and during the winter months Kertész edited the film. I stood by while he explained to me the technical business of cutting and splicing. In April, 1923, "Sodom and Gomorrah" was shown in the movie theatres of Vienna. It was a smash hit in the city. But I flunked anatomy lab.

My father was furious. He turned on Mother. "I warned you!" he shouted. "It is your fault!"

Mother tried to appease him.

"All right, all right," he said finally. "But now the hocus-pocus is over. *Verstanden!*"

I told Kertész and he was furious, too. "Your petit-bourgeois father! He cannot grasp what his son has achieved! A career! Fame!"

Soon I noticed it myself. At first, I thought it was only accidental. While sitting with Kertész in the Café Arkaden, a student café located near the university, I would see people point at us and whisper. Kertész had a considerable reputation, and I was not surprised at the public attention he was given. But once when I was waiting for him a young lady approached me and asked for an autograph. I must have looked blank as I signed my name, and the girl looked quite disappointed. "I thought you were Lot," she said. Happily, I signed my pseudonym, and other visitors of the café came crowding round. The same thing happened when I was sitting on a bench of the Votivpark, near the university. And if I had needed an additional confirmation of my popularity, I received it soon.

The *Studentenkrawalle*, anti-Semitic student demonstrations, were a biannual occurrence at registration time, when nationalist students attempted to prevent Jewish students from entering the university—a kind of carnival watched by hundreds of Viennese outside the university building. When I went up the outside steps of that building to register for the summer semester, I was immediately stopped by a long-legged student wearing the fraternity cap of a nationalist student society. He asked me if I was Jewish, and I answered that it was none of his business. A brawl ensued, and the proctor's men who were on duty came over and conducted the two of us to the dean's office.

The dean, a professor of pharmacology, had a beard enveloping most of his face. He asked who had initiated the fight.

I said it was I.

"Don't you know that disturbances in these halls are prohibited?" he thundered at me.

I told him the circumstances, and added that certainly I had a right to register.

"You should have complained," the dean said.

"To whom?"

"To the proctor's men—don't you know that?"

"They arrived only after that brute—"

"Don't use such expressions. I suspend you for the coming semester."

"But *Herr Dekan*," I protested.

The dean took off his eyeglasses and wiped them with great care. After putting them back on his nose, he studied my face. Then, around his fleshy lips, partly hidden by his beard, a smile appeared. "Are you by any chance Lot?" he said.

More trouble, I thought, for I had broken university regulations. But I had no other choice than to answer yes.

"Sentence suspended," the dean said.

———

My summer vacation was ruined; I had to prepare for the anatomy exam in the fall. The lab remained open during the summer and I had much to make up. I met often with Kertész at the Café Arkaden. "Sodom and Gomorrah," in spite of its critical success, was not doing well at the box office. Vienna, the proverbial capital of music and the arts, had not established a reputation in moviemaking. The Pathé Frères of France, UFA (Universum-Film-Aktiengesellschaft) of Berlin, Hollywood, and even little Denmark were more recognized on the world market. I half listened to Kertész explaining why while I read about heart valves, and muscles and their innervations.

One night, Kertész arrived at the café earlier than usual. He moved around on his chair uneasily. "I've an idea. Listen," he said.

I looked up from my book.

"It's raining incessantly, but the payroll goes on. I'm fed up with the Laaerberg. I've decided to shoot a couple of films at Lake Como. Eternal sun . . ."

"And what has that to do with me?" I asked.

"A couple of Ferenc Molnár comedies. Would you come along?"

"Out of the question!" I pointed at my book.

"You wouldn't have to work all the time. You could study, too."

"I am staying right here!" I pounded the table.

"Hundred schillings!" Kertész narrowed his eyes.

Money was no longer a temptation to me. The fortunes of my family had changed. The peace treaty of Saint-Germain, concluded in 1919 between Austria and the victorious Allied powers, ceded parts of western Hungary to Austria and established a new province, the Burgenland. In 1923, Father had regained his old position, and I was now fully supported from home. I told Kertész so.

"It's not the money," he said apologetically. "I meant it only as a token of appreciation." He smiled. "Aren't you flattered, you blockhead? Well, think it over. Lake Como instead of this terrible Vienna. Look out the window. Brrr."

And he went on talking about his plans. The perfect pied piper, I thought, unmoved. But then, little by little, he pulled me once again into his sphere. After all—couldn't I take part in these movies and at the same time study for my exam?

I travelled to Sauerbrunn, a little watering place, now the temporary capital of Burgenland. It was not hard to persuade Mother, but how to win over Father? My parents lived in a spacious apartment on the second floor of a building whose first floor was taken up by Father's offices. On the veranda overlooking a garden with apple, pear, cherry, and walnut trees, Mother and I discussed stratagems till late at night, while Father still worked in his office. I looked tired, Mother said, and Father would certainly not object to my taking a vacation in the sunny south. That would be the best line to take. "But will you also study?" she asked anxiously.

THE movie productions at Lake Como proceeded according to plan. I was now an old hand. I played Hungarian cavalry officers and jealous husbands with skill. Even Kertész seemed to be satisfied, although he did not commend me; in business, he kept a proper distance between himself and the staff. During my free time, I swam in the azure-blue lake. Nights, I danced with Lot's younger daughter, again my partner, in spite of Kertész' explicit order that the cast must be in bed at ten. Once, he caught us and created a scandal in the presence of other guests at the bar, who knew us and enjoyed the scene. As a consequence, we were locked at nine in separate rooms. Now, finally, I studied anatomy.

At the end of August, the troupe travelled home. Father and Mother were both pleased at the way I looked. "You have a good suntan," Father said. "But I hope you're ready for the exam." I assured Mother that everything had gone well—movie acting and also studying. We agreed that Father, who never went to the movies, would not find out about my escapade.

The first week of October, I passed anatomy and was through with the basic sciences. I was ready for the Allgemeines Krankenhaus—the teaching hospital. It was built at the order of Josef II, the enlightened Hapsburg emperor, in the seventeen-seventies. A few buildings had been added, but in my time it did not look very different from the day it had been erected: small buildings separated by seven courtyards, patches of green. The air always carried the smell of iodine and carbolic acid. In spring, when the acacia trees bloomed, their scent mingled with the smell of the medications.

My heart bumped when I first placed my stethoscope on the chest of a patient, when I watched the first operation, when I heard for the first time the cry of a newborn baby. I was proud to be a student of the venerable Vienna Medical School. During the day, I was fully occupied with attending lectures and work in the hospital, but when eve-

UNIVERSITY OF WINNIPEG
LIBRARY
515 Portage Avenue
Winnipeg, Manitoba R3B 2E9

ning came I found myself in a trolley car travelling to the Laaerberg.

I was determined to stick to my medical studies and not to be swayed by any temptation. Even Kertész seemed reconciled to my decision. While he edited the rolls of film, swearing steadily about omissions either by the actors or by himself, he seemed to listen to my accounts of my day's work. Then, in the projection room, we watched the films, and, with a side glance at me, Kertész would often murmur that I had done a fine job. Later, settling down in the office, we drank Turkish coffee, often long after midnight. Next morning, I would wake up sleepy and tired. Once, in a lecture on gynecology (Professor Kermauner, a great scholar, was an unstimulating lecturer), I was awakened by the Professor himself. Shamed before my laughing colleagues, I apologized and swore to myself that from here on I would be in bed early. I kept my promise for a few days. Then I travelled again to the Laaerberg.

In April, arriving at the dormitory for a lecture, I was called to the telephone. It was Mother. She sounded despondent. Father had found out about my summer excursion. How? He had been congratulated about his "great actor son." Father was so angry he would not even speak to her. I should think what to say, she warned me; she had run out of all possible explanations.

I thought of not going home for the weekend, but then I decided I might as well face the inevitable. I arrived on the afternoon train, after lunch (lunch is the main meal in Central Europe), to have time to talk with Mother alone. Father had not changed, she said. He still refused to speak to her. But, in spite of her desperate mood, Mother could not repress her feelings: she had seen the movies and she thought I was very good. We did not have long to talk; the telephone rang and I was summoned to Father's office.

When I went in, he only nodded, sitting behind his desk, on which papers, letters, files were arranged in impeccable order. Unperturbed by my presence, he signed one paper after another. I waited for his wrath to fall on me. It never did. After a few minutes, he placed his pen on the desk and fixed me with his gray-green eyes. "If you go on as you are," he said without raising his voice, "you will be regarded as a fool. No one will ever take you seriously —neither medical school nor your movie people. No one can serve two masters [*Niemand kann zwei Herren dienen*]. You must make up your mind. You are already twenty-two."

So I made up my mind: medicine. And the more I progressed in my studies, the more engrossed I became. My contact with Kertész did not cease—the contrary. We met more often than ever in the Café Arkaden, where we spoke about many things, including moviemaking. I even signed autographs—but my past achievements belonged to a closed past. Once, he said casually that he contemplated making a picture about a doctor's life, and I thought he was watching me from the corner of his eye.

One day, I was called out from a surgery lecture. A messenger was waiting in the hall with a note. I should come immediately to the Laaerberg. I thought there was something physically wrong with Kertész and left at once.

He was waiting for me in his office, looking perfectly healthy and dressed in his gray checked holiday suit (ordinarily, at all seasons, he wore a short-sleeved black sweater). Without saying a word, he handed me a telegram. I read it. UFA had invited him to Berlin for a conference. "Congratulations," I said. I was really happy for him.

"Come on," he said impatiently. "My car is waiting to take us to the station."

"What do you mean?"

"Don't ask questions." He pushed me ahead of him to the door.

"But I don't have even an extra shirt," I protested.

"You'll get it in Berlin."

The train ride lasted fourteen hours. We rode in a sleeper, Kertész in the upper berth. I scarcely closed my eyes the whole night. Kertész talked incessantly, climbing up and down the ladder—now for a glass of water, another time for a bottle of cognac; he never stopped smoking. I was glad when the first daylight filtered through the window curtains and I could get up. I was hungry—I realized that I hadn't eaten since lunch the previous day.

We arrived at the Potsdamer Bahnhof at five in the afternoon. There I sent a telegram to my parents to say where I was and that I would explain in a letter the circumstances of my trip. At the film company we were greeted by the *Regisseur*—the director—a tall, stout man. UFA was always searching for new talent, he said, and they had been watching Kertész' work in the Sascha Company with interest. However, the Sascha Company was small, comparatively unknown. Before UFA could offer Kertész a contract, he would have to prove himself in Berlin. As a test, they would like him to direct the first part of a film with a Hungarian theme (it was called something like "Sunset on the Puszta"). He was to start immediately; in a neighboring room, half a dozen cameramen and technicians were waiting for him. Then the *Regisseur* turned to me and asked who I was. Kertész said that I was the pillar of the Sascha Company. He had thought they would want to meet me.

Without even taking time to wash up, Kertész went to work. At first he was jittery, but within a day or two he found himself—authoritative, abusive, ingenious. Only at night, when we had a nightcap together, did he have doubts. Would he get the contract? I wrote home assuring my parents that my Berlin excursion was no relapse into the movie world.

One night three weeks after our arrival in Berlin, Kertész stumbled into my room. His face was deadly pale and he was perspiring profusely. With trembling fingers, he took a sheet of paper from his pocket—his contract. It was high time for me to get back to medical school.

During the train ride back to Vienna, Kertész slept like a child, although as a precaution I took the upper berth. I could not sleep this time, either. Had I been honest with myself? The weeks in Berlin had wakened my dormant feelings for the world of the screen. Revolutionary changes were taking place—indoor ateliers, the first experiments with sound. The UFA people had been kind to me; I had been given a film test. Now I was going back to the dreary world of everyday—another year in medical school. And then? A doctor, one among thousands.

Kertész' contract with the Sascha Film Company had just expired, and he was winding up his affairs on the Laaerberg. We met daily until his departure. I went with him to the railway station to see him off for Berlin.

For several months after that, I had no news from Kertész. I knew that he did not believe in letter writing ("a petit-bourgeois habit," he would say). It was in June, 1925 (I remember the date, because the day before I had passed my pathology exam), that I received a telegram from him. It had been sent from Berlin, and I tore it open impatiently. I read: "YOUR CONTRACT READY STOP COME IMMEDIATELY STOP MICHAEL KERTÉSZ UFA."

I took the next train to Sauerbrunn. There was no question in my mind—I would go to Berlin. Father was not at home, and Mother was preparing dinner. I gave her the telegram, scrutinizing her face as she read it. She had aged. Her diabetes, recently discovered, had taken a great toll. She read the telegram again and again, her hands shaking.

"I understand, Richard," she said at last in her gentle voice. "It is a great honor. But"—she sighed deeply—"finish your studies first. A doctor can always become an actor, but an actor can never become a doctor."

———◆———

YEARS passed, and decades. I did not hear from Kertész after I wrote explaining that I must finish my studies. But my early experience in the theatre haunted me. As a country doctor, I arranged amateur performances at country fairs. Later, on the Ivory Coast, where I was a colonial surgeon, I amazed my fellow-colons once when, with natives as actors, I produced a Ferenc Molnár comedy. Still later, in an American children's camp where I was camp doctor, I directed the children in a Sholom Aleichem play.

In the early forties, "Casablanca" was a much celebrated movie in America. It had been directed by a Michael Curtiz. One day, I saw his picture in a magazine—a late-middle-aged man, with a quizzical smile around the lips. Wasn't he my old director, Kertész? I wrote to him in Hollywood. No answer. I must have been mistaken, I thought. But years later, returning from a summer vacation, I found among the letters that had accumulated during my absence a note in Hungarian:

Sorry I couldn't answer earlier. Always busy. Now, while visiting a playwright in New York, I called your number. No luck. You were away. I would have liked to meet you, talk about the old times, the Laaerberg, "Sodom and Gomorrah." Wasn't it good to be young? I was happy to hear that you have a family and a good practice. But I must say that you had talent—blockhead.

I was sorry to have missed him. Soon, I read in the papers that Michael Curtiz had died.

Fellow-American

I N 1923, I spent a wonderful summer near St. Gilgen, that
magnificent town on the western shores of the Wolfgangsee, a large lake in the environs of Salzburg. I was a
medical student at the time and had been offered a post as
a doctor's aide in a camp for teen-age apprentices, with the
provision that I double as lifeguard. I was a good swimmer
and passed the qualifying examination easily. The camp
was about three hours' walking distance from St. Gilgen.
Several times a week, I would set out with a dozen boys
and hike along winding mountain roads through a pine
forest. The air was crisp and aromatic. Sunlight, wherever
it could penetrate the dense thicket of pine needles, spar-
kled on grass and wild flowers. When we were almost
there, the church tower of St. Gilgen would come in sight,
and then the lake itself. In seconds, we would change into

our swimming suits and plunge into the cold mountain water.

Everyone has had such simple pleasures in his youth. I planned to go back, but somehow the opportunity never came until I attended a medical congress in Paris nearly thirty years later. I would have three weeks between the end of the congress and the return of my chartered flight to New York, and, trying to think of a vacation spot where I could rest, I was struck by a longing to see St. Gilgen again. I wrote to Austrian friends, Ernst and his wife, Barbara, and asked them to join me there.

In 1950, Austria was occupied by the four victorious powers, and American personnel occupied hotels in all summer resorts in the neighborhood of Salzburg. It was impossible to get reservations at the Excelsior, the only hotel in St. Gilgen that came up to international standards. We tried to find accommodations in other towns around the Wolfgangsee, but without success. Finally, Ernst wrote that he had found a room for himself and Barbara in a small inn and a room for me in another inn across the lake from them. The inn where I would stay was named Gasthaus zum Goldenen Ochsen—not a hotel *"für verwöhnte Amerikaner,"* Ernst warned me, but an unpretentious country hostel with neither plumbing nor electricity. But so clean one could eat *Salzburger Nockerln* off the floor, and the *Nockerln*, incidentally, would be the best to be had anywhere. He and Barbara would row across the lake to take their meals with me at the Golden Oxen.

I am a poor traveller. During the almost thirty hours' flight from New York to Paris in a converted Flying Tiger, I couldn't sleep for a second. And the medical congress was the noisiest I had ever attended. I longed for quiet and the cold waters of the Wolfgangsee. On the Orient Express from Paris to Salzburg, I spent another twenty-four sleepless hours. But at last I was on a local train bound for St. Gilgen.

I arrived at sunset to find the blue Wolfgangsee changing to a fiery red. At the inn, Ernst and his wife awaited me with some impatience. We hadn't seen each other since the Anschluss, a time when they—both Aryans—had behaved heroically in defense of my family. Ernst's hair had turned from brown to steel gray. He remarked that I had gained weight but otherwise hadn't changed a bit. His wife, fifteen years his junior, laughed as she appraised me. "He looks somehow *amerikanisch,*" she said. "And twelve years older." I said that she hadn't changed at all, although she had actually gained much weight since I had seen her last, in Mattersburg, the town near Vienna where I had formerly practiced.

The proprietor introduced himself as Herr Wiedmayer and took my two suitcases up one flight to my room, telling me en route that all six rooms of the inn were occupied by guests. I wondered idly who they might be. My room was simply and frugally furnished—two chairs beside an unpolished table, a *lavoir* and giant pitcher in one corner, a small night table with a candle in a silver holder on it, and a huge bed piled with quilts almost to the low ceiling.

After washing up, I went down to dinner. The dining room was small; a fading print of old Emperor Franz Josef hung on one wall, a sepia waterfall on another. Through a high window, the view looking down the lake was superb. Several couples were seated. We eyed one another with casual interest. They were all Europeans, I guessed, except for one couple who might be Americans. I was joined by Ernst and Barbara. Dinner was superb—tender boiled beef, and for dessert the best *Topfenstrudel* I had ever eaten. Ernst's prediction had been right. He and Barbara watched the delight on my face as I ate. Afterward, seated outside at a table facing the lake, we told each other our experiences of the past twelve years. Ernst, a well-known opponent of the Nazis, had had a brutal time under Hitler. I, in turn, told about my family's travels and tribulations in Europe and in Africa, where I worked as a colonial doctor, and about our escape to America after the defeat of France.

Ernst and Barbara were fascinated by the saga of our initial difficulties in the New World and eventual adjustment, but I could see a worried look coming over Ernst's face. "You have found a new place to live," he said, "but Austria will always be your homeland."

"Well," his wife observed, "I'm not so sure. Richard cuts everything, even meat, with the fork. And I'll wager he even likes orange juice *before* breakfast."

"Let's not talk about superficialities," Ernst said. "Tell me, Richard, what about your son. How did Peter get along? One of the greatest crimes the Nazis committed was making children homeless. They were simply torn out from their soil!"

"Believe it or not," I said, "Peter was the first of us to find roots in America. He learned English, American style, in no time. As a matter of fact, you wouldn't know him from any other American boy."

"He plays baseball?" Ernst asked.

"He is wild about it."

"Soccer?"

"No soccer."

Ernst shook his head. We both were soccer players once, and later enthusiastic fans. *"Da kann man halt nichts machen,"* he said with resignation.

I quickly assured Barbara that my wife still kept a Viennese kitchen and would be grateful to receive new recipes. She promised to write down several, and Ernst seemed a bit heartened.

It was past midnight, and I had a long day behind me.

My friends thoughtfully said they were weary and suggested that we all retire. I accompanied them to their boat and watched them row off into the darkness.

I WENT up to my room, undressed quickly, and slid beneath the quilts. It was a cool night such as I remembered from the past. I extinguished the candle and fell asleep instantly.

Sometime later, I awoke. I could hear a whimpering from very near—a child's cry, I thought at first. But when I was fully awake I could distinguish the sound more clearly—it was the whine of a dog from the room at my left. This was followed by a whine of a different note, and another, and still another. The quartet of whines changed into barks. I covered my head with the quilts, but the noise penetrated. An hour went by, and the barking hadn't diminished.

I love dogs. As a matter of fact, I'm mad about dogs. I lay there for a time, deliberating, before I decided to get up and speak to the innkeeper. Then I couldn't find matches to light the candle; in my hurry to get into bed, I must have dropped them. I crept out into the corridor, then groped my way down the creaking staircase. A few feet beyond the stairs, I overturned a chair. Instantly, a door sprang open, and there stood Herr Wiedmayer—round-faced, with typical old-country mustache. In one hand he held a lighted candle and in the other a hunting gun. "*Wea is denn do?*" he shouted, in his Salzburgian accent.

"It's I," I answered. "The guest who arrived last night."

"*Gottseidank,*" he said, letting the gun arm fall limp. "What are you doing here?"

I told him my trouble.

He lifted the candlestick and scratched his head with his thumb. "Unfortunately," he began, "it's nothing new. The people before you also complained—to no avail."

"Then give me another room."

"I have none. All are taken."

I had forgotten. "Why did you rent that room when you knew—"

He shrugged. "It's a brief season. One must make a living."

"Who the hell is in that room, besides the dogs?"

"Americans. They moved in in May—a month ago. Obviously, they couldn't find accommodations at the Excelsior. And, *Gottseisgeklagt*, they'll stay until September!" He put the gun and candlestick on a table and began to wring his hands.

"Has no one ever complained to *them?*"

"My guests are Austrians, and only a few speak bits of English. People *did* complain. The American insisted that the dogs must stay with him."

"American or not, I'm on my vacation, Herr Wiedmayer, and it's your job to talk to him. You're the proprietor, aren't you?"

He threw up his hands. "How can you ask me to do that? Do you want me to start a new war with America?"

"I don't expect you to start a war, but something has to be done. Do you have a place to put the dogs overnight?"

"Yes—a nice, clean, warm space right behind the kitchen."

"Who are these Americans, anyway?"

"He must be a *Grosskopferter*," said Herr Wiedmayer, standing on tiptoe and puffing out his chest. "He's employed with the Americans in Salzburg. Twice a week, a messenger brings him papers to sign."

"We must talk to him," I said firmly.

"But I don't want to offend the American," Herr Wiedmayer protested.

"Look," I said. "I am also an American!"

Herr Wiedmayer smiled. "Maybe so, but those are *real* Americans."

I gave up, accepted the lighted candle that Herr Wiedmayer proffered, and returned to my room. The dogs were still audible, but I sank into my bed and fell asleep at once.

When I awoke at nine, the sun was shining on the quilts. I got up and went to the window to look at the smooth water of the lake, a sight that cheered me. Then I washed my hands and face in the *lavoir*. After breakfast, I would take a long swim in lieu of a bath.

The moment I stepped out into the corridor, four dogs ran from the neighboring room. They were French poodles, two miniatures and two standards—all black, slender, beautiful animals, their heads held high. They were followed by the man and woman I had thought at dinner might be American—the man tall and strong, with thinning brown hair and a tiny mustache, about forty-five or so, the woman petite, blond, and pretty, at least ten years younger than her husband. She wore a dirndl but looked decidedly non-Austrian.

I said good morning, and they returned the greeting. For a moment, I thought I would settle the matter of the dogs there and then, but I lost heart. I simply looked at the poodles with deepest friendship and hoped the coming night would be better.

The Americans were again my neighbors in the dining room, at the closest table. The dogs ran around the room, wagging their short tails, and one of them came to lick my hand. They were quickly called to order by their master, and during the meal they were well behaved.

When Ernst and Barbara joined me shortly, I told them about the night's adventure and tossed it off by saying that

I was certain it wouldn't happen again. Ernst said that poodles were unpredictable. He was greatly concerned over my comfort, since he had secured the room for me. I saw immediately that I should have kept the affair to myself. "Try another night," he said. "If it happens again, speak to them. Don't wait for Herr Wiedmayer. Innkeepers always try to avoid being involved in their guests' disputes."

I had a marvellous day with my friends. We swam a great deal, paddled around the lake in their boat, and had lunch in a little restaurant on an offshore island. Dinner at the inn was again superb, and we talked until after midnight.

———————

THE dogs began at two o'clock. I got up and paced. There was no point in returning to bed. I sat upright in a chair, where I napped for a few minutes at a time through the rest of the night. Finally, the sky over the lake turned purple and red, and the sun rose from behind the eastern shore. At nine, I stepped out of my room just in time to see the poodles running to the staircase. I introduced myself to my neighbors, saying that we seemed to be the only Americans at the inn.

"Browne," the man responded, holding out his hand.

"Your poodles are remarkable," I said.

"Thank you," Mrs. Browne said.

"I am very fond of dogs," I began. I told them about my nocturnal ordeal and about the clean, warm space behind the kitchen.

"It's out of the question," Browne said, stiffening. He brushed past me. "Sorry, no," he said without looking back.

He suddenly reminded me of a colleague at my hospital

—a cold, unpleasant perfectionist of a man. Too late, I grew angry.

I must have looked disturbed when I reached my table, although I tried to conceal my anger from Ernst and Barbara.

"The dogs?" Ernst asked.

I gave an evasive answer and began to eat my breakfast.

The Brownes were involved in a conversation. Browne was gesticulating. His wife cautioned him to talk more quietly, which seemed only to aggravate matters. "Let him hear," he said loudly. "These—these refugees! First they sneak into our country, and before you know it they're taking over."

I must have turned pale, and Ernst, who was watching me fixedly without understanding a word Browne spoke, now insisted on knowing what had happened.

I told him.

In another moment, Ernst had jumped up from his seat. He was very tall, and in the small dining room he looked like a giant. Ernst had a very distinguished military background. He was one of the most decorated soldiers of World War I and had received the Order of Maria Theresa, which carried with it the title of baron. Later, he became a prominent Social Democrat and republican, but time hadn't diminished his martial temperament. "You Americans defeated the Nazis!" he shouted in German at Browne. "And now you're bringing another brand of Nazism into our country! You should be ashamed!"

Whether or not Browne understood German, he fully comprehended the word "Nazi." He leaped up, and the two tall men stood face to face. "What did you say? Are you calling me a Nazi? I was in Normandy on D Day, and you dare call me a Nazi?"

Herr Wiedmayer appeared out of nowhere and forced his way between the two men. "*Aba maine Hearrn,*" he pleaded. "You're on your vacations. Have pity on me. I'm a widower. I must do everything myself—cooking, baking, gardening. Everything is on my poor shoulders. I've a short season. So please don't . . ."

At this appeal, Ernst took his seat, and so did Mr. Browne. We gulped down our coffee and got up quickly. As we passed our neighboring table, I heard Mr. Browne mutter something. I paused and said quietly, "I'm going to write my congressman and tell him how American representatives behave abroad."

I don't know where the idea came from. I am not one to demand satisfaction by calling for the store manager or maître d'hôtel. I had never said such a thing before in my life. Only recently, I had studied the American Constitution for my citizenship examination, and maybe the power invested in the legislative branch of government made an impression on me.

My friends and I were standing on the lake shore when an old Plymouth passed by. Browne was at the wheel, and the miniature poodles sat on Mrs. Browne's lap. The standards looked at us inquisitively through the back window.

Ernst could not quiet down the entire day. He spoke steadily about the kind of democracy that was being imported to Austria. I would try to explain that one should not generalize; there were good and bad Americans as there were good and bad Austrians.

Dinner that evening was an awkward affair. The Brownes appeared early, said nothing during their meal, and left hurriedly. I thought Mrs. Browne looked a bit pale, and she coughed often, which I supposed to be a sign of nervousness. My friends boarded their boat early, and I went to bed at nine.

That night, I slept through and was up at seven, the first guest in the dining room. I asked Herr Wiedmayer for a cup of coffee and said I would have breakfast later.

"How did you achieve it?" he whispered.

I looked blank.

"Come and see," he said, and he led me to a small room next to the kitchen.

It must have served ordinarily as a kind of storeroom. Now a mattress was on the floor, and there the poodles lay, playing with rubber toys. They seemed quite happy, and when Herr Wiedmayer let me out into the garden they followed. I had my coffee there under a tree, and together Herr Wiedmayer and I watched the dogs gambolling.

"When did it happen?" I asked.

"Last night—after dinner," Herr Wiedmayer whispered. He kept looking anxiously in all directions, and at a quarter to nine he rushed the dogs back to their quarters.

I was sitting with my friends at the breakfast table when Browne came down the stairs, alone. He went for his poodles and then ate his breakfast, staring gloomily at three poached eggs. I saw Herr Wiedmayer taking a tray upstairs. They've had an argument about this, I thought, or she's too embarrassed to appear. When I went up to change into my swimming trunks, I heard Mrs. Browne coughing and decided it was, after all, a cold that kept her in.

Herr Wiedmayer confirmed this. "*Jo*," he said. "People from the city don't listen to warnings from people who should know. I always say, 'Watch out, the nights are cool in the mountains!' "

———

THE next morning after breakfast, I saw a man with a doctor's bag talking with Mr. Browne in the corridor outside my room. The doctor spoke in broken English, and it appeared that Browne was having difficulty understanding him. It was professional habit that made me step toward them with the offer to make things clearer to the patient's husband. I should have known better. Mr. Browne interrupted me and said coldly, "Leave us alone and mind your own damn business."

My Austrian colleague looked bewildered at Browne's tone, and as I retreated he accompanied me, explaining that his patient had a very bad cold indeed—bronchitis—and also an intestinal ailment that produced abdominal distress and occasional vomiting. All in all, probably some viral disease, he concluded as he walked down the stairs. Browne followed sullenly. For the doctor's sake, I thought it best to ignore Browne's rudeness, but at the same time I decided to mind my own business thereafter.

The next morning, Herr Wiedmayer reported that Mrs. Browne's condition had become worse. The doctor thought she had pneumonia and advised hospitalization. Browne refused. Four more days passed. I encountered the doctor several times. He looked worried, but I didn't ask questions and I wasn't given any information.

On the evening of the fourth day, I went to Salzburg with my friends and attended a splendid performance of "The Magic Flute." It ended at eleven, and by the time the local train arrived back at St. Gilgen it was half past one. As soon as I reached the top of the stairs, walking as quietly as I could, the door next to mine opened and Browne stepped out, his face drawn and pale.

"I've been waiting for you—Doctor," he said in a hoarse voice. "Please look at my wife. I think she's dying."

I went into my room, took a stethoscope from my suitcase, and hurried next door. Mrs. Browne looked very ill indeed. Her round, pretty face had grown thin, and her nose seemed more pointed. She was breathing heavily and was semiconscious, but she recognized me. "Help me," she whispered.

We lifted her up. I listened to her chest, which was filled with *râles*. Her temperature was a hundred and five. I was ready to agree with the diagnosis made by my colleague, but while examining the patient I discovered something odd—small rose-colored spots between the nipples and the umbilicus. On touch, the spots faded. I felt for the spleen. It was enlarged below the costal margin and very soft. The pulse rate was disproportionately low for the temperature. I could hardly believe what the symptoms indicated—typhoid fever.

I gave Mr. Browne my diagnosis and told him that a drug called Chloromycetin, developed by an American company only a short time before, could save his wife. It was not yet available through commercial channels and would not be found in Austria at all except in American Army hospitals. The hospital at Salzburg must surely have it. I told Browne to stay at his wife's bedside and asked for the keys to his Plymouth.

There was no phone at the Golden Oxen. I drove to the Excelsior and from there called Salzburg. A sleepy female voice answered—the night nurse. I introduced myself and asked for the doctor in charge. Another sleepy voice—the doctor. I explained the case.

"Army personnel?" he asked.

"No," I said, "but it's an American."

"Sorry—for Army personnel only."

"Do you have Chloromycetin?"

"Yes, but—"

I broke in. "I'll be there soon."

It took me over two hours to reach Salzburg along the difficult mountainous roads. At the hospital, I stormed through the door and soon confronted the doctor, who didn't look older than twenty. He repeated his argument.

"The woman is dying," I said.

"Sorry," the doctor said. He was by now quite awake and was trying to be authoritative in the presence of an older colleague.

"How many Chloromycetin tablets do you have?" I persisted.

He looked at me for a moment before answering. "Fifty altogether."

"Look," I said, "you can get more—from Parke, Davis or Washington or somewhere. You must give them to me!"

"But—" His face began to flush with irritation.

I summoned all the restraint I had to keep from shaking the youngster by the shoulders. Then I said quietly and very slowly, "Do you want me to report this to my congressman?"

I HAD never had any experience with Chloromycetin, but I had read the literature on it. I gave two tablets to Mrs. Browne at six in the morning, as soon as I arrived back at the inn, and another two at noon. She was in extremely poor condition and often lost consciousness. At six in the evening, I repeated the dosage. When I took her temperature, I saw it had come down to a hundred and two. By eleven, she was breathing easily and had regained full consciousness. Nevertheless, I decided to continue my vigil for the night, and Browne said he would stay up also.

Around midnight, Herr Wiedmayer came to the door. "*Aba maine Hearrn*, you must eat something. You haven't eaten anything the whole day."

We went down to the dining room, but I wasn't hungry nor was Browne. After eating a few bites of roast chicken, we both pushed our plates away.

"Would you care for a drink?" Browne asked. "Scotch?"

"Anything," I said.

He went up to his room and returned with a large bottle of Vat 69. "On the rocks, Doctor?"

"Yes."

Herr Wiedmayer, who was watching the scene, went to the kitchen. I heard him cutting pieces of ice from a large block in the icebox. Presently, he returned with a pitcherful. "*Amerikaner* like *Schnaps* on ice," he said, grinning. He placed the pitcher on the table and then set down a couple of candles, after which he bade us good night.

Browne and I sat at the table drinking our Scotch in silence. We took turns visiting the patient. At two, I gave her another dose of Chloromycetin.

After Browne's next visit, he finally spoke. "Any hope?"

I nodded yes.

"I'd hate to lose her," he said, looking at his drink. "There's no one else. No kids, that is. Just the two of us— and the dogs."

There was a long, uncomfortable pause. I was about to say something reassuring when Browne continued. "You've probably seen many cases of typhoid, haven't you?"

"Some." And I told him that I had treated sporadic cases during my practice as a country doctor in Austria, and later as a physician in the French colonies. Most of my experience with typhoid, however, had come still later, in a concentration camp in Morocco.

"Morocco! What were you doing there?"

"The ship, which was owned by the Vichy government, that was supposed to take us away from Europe was turned back by the British. We ended up in Morocco."

Again a pause. The quiet was interrupted occasionally by coughing from upstairs. Mr. Browne looked exhausted. There were large bags under his eyes.

"She'll be all right, I'm sure," I said.

He relaxed in his chair for the first time. "And when did you finally get to the States?" he said.

"In 1941," I said.

"Like it?" he asked. "The States?"

"Oh, yes," I said. "At first, it was tough—you know, learning a new language, passing the State Medical Board Exam."

"You mean you had to start from scratch?"

"Yes," I said. "I suppose every immigrant starts from scratch. I suppose your forefathers—when did they arrive?"

"Long ago."

"On the Mayflower?"

"Not on the Mayflower exactly, but they arrived in the middle of the seventeenth century—from France."

"Why do you suppose they left?"

"They had to. They were Huguenots."

"Refugees?"

Browne looked me full in the face for a second, then he smiled faintly. "You might put it that way. Would you like another drink?"

Daylight filtered through the window. I extinguished the candle. Suddenly I saw Herr Wiedmayer, rubbing his eyes. "It's five o'clock already," he said, and looked in astonishment at the empty Scotch bottle.

———————◆———————

THE Gasthaus zum Goldenen Ochsen was quarantined for twelve days, the incubation time of typhoid fever. The guests, for the most part, didn't mind. The food remained excellent. Herr Wiedmayer put on the table everything his kitchen could produce—*Schnitzels, Apfel* and *Kirschenstrudel,*

Torten, and, of course, *Salzburger Nockerln.* I was unhappy only because I couldn't see Ernst and Barbara, and since the inn had no telephone we couldn't even talk with one another; we had to rely on correspondence. Ernst was furious about the whole affair. His letters were full of "that *Schweinehund*" and "that Fascist" who, among other things, was responsible for ruining our vacations. He ignored all references to my peaceable relations with Browne.

Browne was a good swimmer, and we swam daily in the Wolfgangsee. The weather stayed superb, sunny and mild—quite unusual, everyone remarked, for the Salzkammergut, the chain of lakes near Salzburg. The twelve days passed quickly, and so did my vacation time. No further cases of typhoid had developed, and I made preparations to leave.

One morning, I closed my two suitcases and began a round of farewells. Browne had offered to drive me to the rail station at Salzburg.

Herr Wiedmayer shook my hand, saying in his remarkable dialect, *"Mia brauchn an guadn Dokta,"* and urged me to stay on.

I said I was flattered that he thought I was a good doctor, but, alas, I had patients waiting for me in New York—and a family.

Finally, I went to say goodbye to Mrs. Browne, who was now able to sit out in the sun in a garden chair, with the poodles dancing around her.

She took my hand and held it. "Thank you from the bottom of my heart," she said.

I mumbled something modest.

"And just think," she said, "my darling dogs might have caught typhoid!"

"No," I said. "It's contagious for humans only."

"Thank heavens." She sighed.

Ernst and Barbara waited on the station platform—I

had written them the time of my departure. Barbara gave me an old Viennese cookbook for my wife. "I hope she will accompany you when you come again," she said. "Men shouldn't be left alone too long."

Soon the train rolled into the station. The Orient Express stops in Salzburg for only a few minutes, and we had little time. Ernst studied my face as he shook my hand firmly and said, "The Austrian air has done you good." Barbara embraced me. "*Auf baldiges Wiedersehn,*" she said.

The Morphinist

WHEN Christmas of 1928 arrived, I was the youngest resident of the medical department in the Hospital of the City of Vienna, and it was not surprising that my seniors should elect me to remain behind while they went off to enjoy the two-day Austrian Christmas. For the first time, I would have the responsibility of the entire department, with its two hundred and fifty patients, and naturally I was frightened.

The day before Christmas, my colleagues left one by one. The chief resident made the afternoon rounds with me to discuss the most important cases. He was already in his ski clothes. "Don't worry, Richard," he said. "I have confidence in you. New admissions are rare during holidays, and if by chance you find yourself in trouble, you can always look things up in the Schnirer." "Medizinal-

Index und Therapeutisches Vademecum," by a Dr. Schnirer, was a medical pocket manual used by generations of
Viennese doctors.

We returned to the *Dienstzimmer*—the doctors' quarters
—on the third floor, where the chief resident picked up his
skis. He would spend the holiday on the Hohe Wand, a
mountain near Vienna. In the doorway, he waved agreea-
bly. "Cheer up, Richard," he said. Then he was off.

From the window, I watched him leave the building,
his skis slung over his shoulder. My feeling of abandon-
ment was intensified by the curtain of falling snow that all
but obscured the buildings across the quadrangle. It had
been storming intermittently for several weeks, and snow
had drifted in places to make a small range of mountains.
The hospital, popularly called Jubiläumsspital, since it was
erected during the sixtieth anniversary of the reign of Emperor Franz Josef, was situated in what was then open
country, an hour's trip by trolley from the center of Vienna. The city fathers had meant well, building their hospital far from the smoky chimney pots and factories, and,
true enough, spring, summer, and autumn were beautiful
in that suburb, especially with the nearby expanse of the
old Tiergarten. But winter was harsh, and the hospital was
often virtually isolated from the rest of the world. It was
difficult to walk from one part of the hospital to another, or
to the dining room, located in a separate building. Winter
of 1928 was one of the worst in memory, and the weather
of the Christmas holidays was the worst of the season.

Night fell early that Christmas Eve. In the *Tagraum*—
the large social room—a mammoth fir tree rose almost to
the high ceiling. For several days, the patients had helped
the Sisters of Charity, who served as nurses, to decorate it
with tiny doughnuts, oranges, figs, dates, candies, and
chocolate bars, all wrapped in multicolored paper. Now it

stood gleaming with a hundred candles—red, green, yellow. "Stille Nacht, Heilige Nacht" sounded through the corridors, and sisters and patients assembled around the tree to pray before dispersing to their rooms.

My evening rounds were about to begin. I set off for the ward where the most serious cases were confined. Sister Pia, the head nurse, awaited me with chart book in hand. She was an elderly woman with a frail, marble-white face and pale-blue eyes, always half closed behind her silver-rimmed spectacles. She was a power in the medical department. Even our chief, a high-ranking internist, would never disregard an opinion pronounced by Sister Pia. She spoke softly, in the dialect of her Sudeten German homeland, and a slight lifting of her head would suffice to stifle any opposition. We young doctors were seldom addressed by her.

I approached her diffidently. She wished me a good evening and turned to lead the way to our first patient. He was a young man in an advanced stage of pneumonia—one of many similar cases in the ward. In those days, pneumonia was the principal cause of death among the acutely ill. Sulfa drugs and antibiotics were unknown, and the disease would take its own prolonged—often fatal— course. As I adjusted my stethoscope, I saw to my embarrassment that my hand was shaking. A short time later, Sister Pia leaned toward me and said in a whisper, "Don't be afraid, Herr Doktor. I remember many, many young doctors in these past forty years who were not so sure of themselves when they started out. Now they are old professors with long, gray beards." She lifted her thin brows and with fragile fingers stroked an imaginary beard. I took a deep breath.

As we walked from bed to bed, Sister Pia made notes and occasionally whispered advice. We continued through the remaining wards until she warned me that it was nearly eight o'clock, when the dining room closed. I could hardly believe that I had already survived several hours.

"Don't rush through your supper," Sister Pia said. "There's a long night ahead."

After dressing in my heavy boots and overcoat for the short trip to the dining room, I pushed out into the snow, which seemed to be falling faster. Perhaps none of my colleagues would be able to return, I thought despondently. In the dining room, only one of three waitresses was on hand to serve during the holidays. Like me, she was the youngest and had been left behind. She was in a peevish mood and looked pointedly at the clock. "It's Christmas Eve," she said, "and I would also like to be with my family."

I promised to eat quickly, and she grudgingly brought the first course—a bowl of chicken soup. As I lifted my spoon, the telephone rang. The waitress answered it and nodded toward me.

The admitting physician, Dr. Kreisler, was on the other end of the wire. "Sorry," he said, "I know you must be eating. Well, an ambulance is on its way with a morphine-poisoning case. Better come over and take a look."

I gestured helplessly at the waitress, and climbed back into my boots and coat. I had not reached the door when the phone rang again, and again it was Kreisler.

"Stay there," he said. "The man died on the way. The ambulance doctor asked if he could leave the corpse in our morgue. I said yes. Do you know the rules? I don't, and I couldn't find anybody in at the office. Anyway, tomorrow a relative or friend, if he has any, will arrange to have the body picked up. Maybe we'll have a *stille Nacht* yet."

My soup had cooled off and was taken back to the kitchen to be reheated. The heavenly scent of *Weihnacht-skuchen* wafted through the room as the kitchen door

opened, and by the time the waitress returned, my hunger
had become quite painful. The minute she placed the bowl
before me, the telephone rang. I got up to answer it. I did
not dare look at her.

This time, I listened to a throaty voice with a heavy
Viennese accent—the night watchman. "Come as fast as
you can," he said.

"What's wrong?"

"He's alive."

"Who?"

"The dead man. After the ambulance leaves, I lock the
door from the outside—it's the rule. Suddenly I hear a
groan. 'Where does it come from?' I ask myself. I listen
again. Now I hear a bump. Well, I think, what goes on in
there? I go in, and Herr Doktor, I can hardly believe my
eyes. The corpse on the table has turned over, and one eye
is squinting!"

Was Herr Hasenbichler sober, I wondered. One met
him at night while he walked his rounds, nodding his head,
a lantern dangling from a soldier's belt. In his faded uniform, decorated with a medal earned in one of the older
wars of the Hapsburg empire, he would have made an ideal
poster for any veterans' organization. But the watchman
was known to like his glass of schnapps. Who would deny
him an extra glass or so on Christmas Eve? I phoned Kreisler for advice.

He laughed. "Don't be a fool, Richard. Hasenbichler,
that old *Frosch*. Look—the ambulance doctor told me he
found twenty empty two-c.c. ampules of morphine on the
patient's night table. And an empty syringe. Forget it."

Kreisler was a senior resident, but still . . . Improbable
as it was, I could not afford to ignore Hasenbichler's account. "Please," I said to the waitress. "Five minutes more.
I'm sure it's a false alarm."

I dressed rapidly and pushed through the snow the

three hundred yards to the morgue, arriving quite winded, just in time to find Hasenbichler locking the door.

"Too late," he said.

So, I thought, I had fallen for his story. I would be the laughingstock of the hospital.

"He is on his stomach all right," Hasenbichler continued, "and the blanket has fallen to the floor. Suddenly he moans and gasps. Like this—'Ahhhh.' Now he's *really* dead."

"Unlock the door," I said sharply.

The morgue was dimly lighted. Several corpses lay on dissection tables, covered by linen. I followed Hasenbichler to a table where a man in a white cotton shirt and wrinkled khaki trousers lay—on his stomach.

"Wasn't he on his stomach to begin with?" I said rather sternly.

Hasenbichler slowly shook his head. "No, Herr Doktor."

"Let's turn him over," I said.

The man's arms fell limp as we did so. I switched on my flashlight and lifted his eyelids. His pupils were pinpoints. With a start, I thought, Those of the dead are dilated to a maximum. But when I applied my stethoscope to the man's chest, I could hear nothing. I held the stethoscope in place while I tried to puzzle out the contradiction. Suddenly I heard a faint beat, like rain striking a distant windowpane. There was a long pause, and then it was repeated. Was I hallucinating? I looked at Herr Hasenbichler. He stood motionless, his lower lip touching his mustache. I glanced around the whitewashed walls and up at the ceiling. Nothing moved. I held my breath. I could hear my own heartbeat. Was it that? I placed the stethoscope again on the man's chest. Now I heard it distinctly —a beat, a pause, a beat. I timed the beats. Only ten in one minute. Six seconds between beats. It seemed impossible. I took a mirror from my pocket and put it at the man's mouth. When I removed it, I must have shouted.

Hasenbichler jumped. *"Was is' denn los?"* he said.

I showed him the mist covering the mirror. At the same moment, I felt triumph and panic. What was to be done next? If I called the medical department, it would take the stretcher-bearers ten minutes to reach the morgue and another ten to return to the hospital. Obviously, treatment had to begin at once. But I had never before been confronted with a case of morphine poisoning. Then I thought of the Schnirer in my pocket. I turned to the chapter on opium poisoning and read:

> Opium and its derivatives depress the respiratory center. The pupils are the size of pinpoints and do not react to light and accommodation. The main symptoms are drowsiness, leading to deep sleep or quasi-unconsciousness, and finally death through paralysis of the respiratory center. Continuous reflex stimulation—slapping, pinching, shaking—can revive the center. Artificial respiration is imperative as first aid. Oxygen and caffeine are the methods of choice.

I also read that the respiratory rate in such cases could diminish to as little as six in a minute, and that the heart rate slowed down accordingly. Was it possible that so sluggish an action could carry enough blood to the heart to keep it beating? I looked up and met Hasenbichler's little eyes, embedded in a thousand tiny wrinkles. You arrogant chap, he seemed to be thinking, you thought you knew everything.

"Give me a hand," I said.

We lifted the man down to the floor and laid him on his back. I started artificial respiration with one hand, and with the other I slapped and pinched the man's face.

Hasenbichler coughed to catch my attention and said, "Excuse me, Herr Doktor, allow me."

I stood up. With hands as big as shovels, Hasenbichler seized the patient's arms high and then dashed them down to his chest, almost crushing it. I watched in wonder. It had sounded much easier in the Schnirer. The man's color remained gray. After a time, I saw large drops of perspiration running down Hasenbichler's face. Reluctantly, he turned the patient over to me for a short while, and then he resumed.

Eventually, I discovered a slight change in the patient's complexion, which began to show a faint flush of pink and gradually deepened. At once I started to pinch and slap his cheeks. Suddenly a deep sigh came from the man, and his chest began moving in and out. I ran to the phone and called my department, asking for Sister Pia.

"Thank heavens," she said. "There you are. It's after ten."

I told her the story, trying to conceal my elation.

"For pity's sake," she said when I finished, her voice rising ever so slightly. "Why didn't you call me at once? The man needs oxygen and more oxygen, and caffeine. But, Herr Doktor Berczeller, what were you thinking of? We are in a hospital!"

I stuttered an apology.

"Never mind," said Sister Pia, once more composed. "The man is alive, and that's all that matters. I'll send a stretcher."

When I returned to the patient, he had just opened his eyes. They were bloodshot, and fluttered with the effort of accommodating to light. His face was puffed, his lips swollen. "Leave me alone, please," he whispered.

"No, sir," said Hasenbichler at my side. "You don't make a fool of me a second time."

Nevertheless, the patient closed his eyes. His breathing instantly diminished. I shook him, and he looked up again. "You must stay awake," I said.

Two attendants arrived with a stretcher, and only when the patient had been placed on it did I realize he was an exceptionally tall man—probably three or four inches over six feet. Fortunately for the bearers, he was also slender. We made a strange procession through the snow—the stretcher first, followed by me and Hasenbichler, holding aloft his lantern.

"Herr Hasenbichler," I said. "How do you feel after saving a human life?"

He chuckled with embarrassment. "Morphine—imagine. How the world has changed. In the old days, fancy people used the shotgun. Do you remember Crown Prince Rudolf and the Vetsera? How could you? You were not even born. Poor people, of course, used the rope. And young maids in lover's grief drank lye. I remember a girl . . . Well, it was long ago."

At the hospital door, he said good night. I saw his lantern bobbing through the snowfall as he resumed his rounds.

———

THE stretcher barely fitted into the old elevator. It was one of those archaic, cagelike structures that projected from the wall. From the ground floor, one could see the moving loops of cable and the jerking ascent of the car. There wasn't room in it for me, so I walked up the three flights of stairs beside the shaft, nearly keeping pace with the car. Sister Pia was waiting at the elevator door, and the patient was swiftly carried to a bed made up in the *Tagraum*.

"Is this the only space we have?" I asked timidly.

"It's better here," she said. "There will be a lot of activity, and why disturb the other patients, Herr Doktor?" She immediately strapped an oxygen mask around the patient's

71

mouth and handed me a syringe filled with caffeine. The patient had again lapsed into unconsciousness, and I began to think that Hasenbichler's gymnastics might have been in vain. But the oxygen and the stimulant worked with surprising speed. In fifteen minutes, the patient opened his eyes again. Meanwhile, Sister Pia questioned me closely about the episode in the morgue. "What do you suppose happened?" she asked. "A man in his condition doesn't spring to life."

"I don't know," I said. "According to Hasenbichler, he was just lying there."

"Those ambulance men, I suppose," she whispered. "They handle the dead like sacks of potatoes. They probably threw our giant on a table, and it must have produced the reflex stimulation to his respiratory center—no?"

I nodded my head, astonished. I had never thought of that possibility.

The Sister's prominent nasolabial folds smoothed out —as close as she could come to a smile.

We still had many other patients on the critical list to attend to, and after putting a nurse in charge of the morphinist Sister Pia led the way to the wards, with a lift of her seagull hat.

When we returned to the *Tagraum*, our patient was fighting the nurse, who was trying to keep the oxygen mask around his mouth. His eyes looked clearer to me, and I decided to experiment without oxygen. He continued breathing evenly, and his pulse had increased to fifty beats a minute. He still had difficulty accommodating to even the weak light in the room and squinted repeatedly. Each time he closed his eyes, I shook him—a sequence that became routine for the next hour. He would look straight into my face and mutter, "Leave me alone, Herr Doktor." Even these few words were enough to reveal a refined German used by upper-class Viennese.

Now that his appearance was returning to normal, I could see that he was a handsome man—about fifty, with thick, graying hair and an oval face. Sister Pia was observing him closely, too, waiting for the moment when she could get information for the admissions office. Finally, he seemed sufficiently awake, and she said she must ask him a few questions.

He turned away from her. "Must it be?" he said mournfully.

"Yes," she answered. "Your name, please."

There was a pause, and then he said, "Bauer, Alfred."

"Your age and occupation?"

"Please, Sister . . ."

Sister Pia pressed the chart to her chest. "We have our rules, Herr Bauer," she said. "Four hours after admission, at the latest, we must have personal data—although we must grant you are here under somewhat unusual circumstances."

I suppressed a smile, but I saw that she did not intend humor.

"You must stay alive. God gave you life, and you should be grateful," she continued, lifting her brows.

"All right," he said wearily. "I'm an electrical engineer —if I find a job. I'm fifty-five. I live alone. I'm single. My nearest relative is a cousin who lives in Linz. Now may I rest, please?"

At this point, I took over for an examination. He could sit up without help, and apart from the effects of the drug he was in perfect physical health. I noted a large scar with irregular edges at the upper part of his abdomen. It looked to me like the mark of dum-dum bullets often seen on the wounded of the First World War. I touched it with my finger.

"It's old, Herr Doktor. What does it matter?" Bauer said.

I continued to make notes on the chart. "Do you use morphine habitually?" I asked. "Was it an accidental overdose, or did you—"

Bauer had closed his eyes. I shook him.

"Doktor, are you a gentleman?" he said.

"You must stay awake."

"A gentleman minds his own business."

Sister Pia whispered into my ear, "It's enough for the time being."

It was two o'clock. In the quiet, one heard only the shuffling steps of the patients walking to and from the lavatories. "Herr Bauer," I said, "you must stay awake. It will be better for both of us. Let's talk. What are you interested in? Politics? Music? Art?"

"I am interested in nothing."

"All right," I said. I had read in my Schnirer that the peripatetic method could be used to foster circulation. (This has long since been abandoned in the medical profession, because it is in fact supposed to cause a drop in blood pressure.) "We're going to take you for a walk."

After the expected protest, Bauer stepped down from his bed. He was indeed a giant—almost a head taller than I—and Sister Pia, who supported his first steps, looked like a tiny child beside him. "What a pity!" she said, looking up at him as though he were a tree.

We began our promenade around the room, walking first in one direction and then in the other. I now understood why Sister Pia had prepared the bed in the *Tagraum*. I told medical anecdotes and tried to interest Bauer in the doctor's problems of keeping people alive. I don't know how long our marathon went on, but suddenly I was too tired to walk another step. Still, the patient had to be kept occupied. I thought of a card game.

Sister Pia produced a pack of cards from a cabinet, and

I sat down at a table, inviting Bauer to take the seat opposite. "What will you have?" I asked, shuffling the cards.
"Einundzwanzig? Mariasch?"

He chose *Mariasch.* I cut the cards and dealt. After a
few plays, I discovered that Bauer was trying to nap behind
his cards.

"Would you rather walk?" I asked in warning.

Little by little, his interest grew—at least, enough to
have a reasonably intelligent game, although occasionally
when he lifted a card to make a play his hand would freeze
in midair. I would wake him, review the play, and the
game would continue. I also tried to get more data on him.
"How did you get onto morphine?" I asked.

He was shuffling cards. He looked at me in surprise.
"You saw the scar. I spent most of the war in hospitals. I
got lots of morphine. After the war, I used it off and on,
mostly when there was trouble. I was in and out of jobs.
You know . . ."

"And the trouble this time? A woman?"

"Oh, no. Why do you want a reason? Don't you believe
a man can wake up one day and decide he's had enough?"

He became agitated, dealt too many cards, and had to
begin again. To regain his humor, I suggested we bet a
groschen a play. He took this up, played with great inten-
sity, and won thirty hands in a row. By this time I could
hardly concentrate, and my forgotten hunger was burning
into my stomach. I recall looking at the darkened corner
where the Christmas tree stood, and the next thing I knew
someone was shaking my shoulder. I looked up into the
smiling face of Bauer. "Your move, Herr Doktor," he said.

Sister Pia had come into the room. She stopped in front
of me. "Doktor," she said, "take a brief rest—even for a
half hour."

"Good idea," said Bauer, collecting the cards.

I knew that I should stay at my post—I was responsible for everything. And yet, if only I could close my eyes for a few minutes . . .

"I'll keep an eye on things," Sister Pia assured me.

I gave a final, appraising look at Bauer. Then I staggered off to the *Dienstzimmer.* There I collapsed, fully clothed, on the bed and passed immediately into a deep slumber.

House doctors sleep with one ear open. Through my dreams I heard a distant crash. Shortly afterward, someone opened the door to my room. Peering through the slits of my eyes, I saw first a burning candle and then the pale face of Sister Pia.

"Doktor," she whispered, "the morphinist."

I leaped up. Sister Pia accompanied me to the *Tagraum,* where patients stood around in their hospital robes waiting, apparently wakened by the crash. Early daylight showed through the window. The morphinist's bed was empty. "Where is he?" I asked.

"There," said Sister Pia, leading me to the staircase. "He broke away from me. . . ."

The space between the staircase and the elevator formed a wide shaft. I looked down and saw a man's figure sprawled at the bottom. Slowly, I began to descend the stairs.

"Do you need me?" Sister Pia asked.

"No," I said.

I shuddered in anticipation of the bloody, fractured body of the morphinist. By the time I reached the bottom of the stairs, I had involuntarily closed my eyes. But when

I opened them there was no blood in sight. The body lay on its stomach, the head turned to one side. I walked up to it. The limbs seemed in normal position, and the facial complexion looked healthier than before. I leaned down. The morphinist was snoring peacefully.

I slapped him smartly on the face. At once he rolled over, stretched his arms, and yawned. In the same instant, I heard a rustling behind me and turned to see Herr Hasenbichler struggling up from a kneeling position. With one hand, he held his hat and with the other he scratched his bald head. "Lately one cannot be sure of one's life," he said, and moaned. "I came in on my morning rounds—it's the rule—and suddenly I feel something heavy falling on my back. Not my back but here." He indicated his right hip. *"Der Strolch.* Why is he picking on me?"

"For God's sakes," I said, "are you all in one piece?"

"Yes," he said, "but my lantern . . ."

The lantern was indeed damaged—the glass broken and the entire metal frame bent. I assured him that he would be issued another, just as good.

I returned to Bauer, who was now snoring on his back. After examining him quickly for fractures, I asked him in a firm voice to wake up.

He opened his eyes and said, "Did you have a nice rest?"

I did not respond, but commanded him to precede me up the stairs. He obeyed without protest. When we entered the *Tagraum,* we saw Sister Pia kneeling at the tree. She finished her prayer, made the sign of the cross in slow motion, and rose. She looked very much shaken. Advancing almost timidly, she studied Bauer from head to toe.

"Merry Christmas," he said, bowing.

I recalled a bed in the storeroom—an old structure with a high railing around it, once probably used for psychiatric patients. I ordered it moved to a private room and took Bauer there under the escort of two attendants. I had not spoken to him since his second resurrection.

"Why are you angry?" he asked. At first, he thought the bed was a joke, but eventually he crawled into it. The railing was equipped with a lock, which I secured. "You don't have much confidence in me," he complained.

I couldn't help but smile. Before I left, I pressed thirty groschen—the money he had won in the card game—into his hand.

In the *Tagraum*, Sister Pia was waiting to begin our morning rounds. She was quite recovered, standing erect, her seagull hat crisp and pert, the chart book pressed to her bosom.

THE morphinist was discharged two days after Christmas. For several weeks, I searched for his name in the daily obituaries. He never came back. As for me, when I appeared at breakfast after the holidays my colleagues greeted me with cheers. To this day, whenever I encounter one of the old group from the Jubiläumsspital, the first thing he says is, "Tell me the story of the morphinist."

Paternity

I was far advanced in my training to become an internist when, in November, 1929, I established my practice in Mattersburg, a town of four thousand inhabitants in the Burgenland province of Austria. I had grown up there, and my longing for my home country remained strong during the years of my absence in Vienna. I was in my last year of residency at the Hospital of the City of Vienna when I learned to my sorrow that old Dr. Frank, the town's Jewish doctor for more than fifty years, had died. The only other doctor in the area—the Gentile doctor—could not provide sufficient medical care for the town and the surrounding villages and hamlets strewn all over the Rosalia Mountains, and impulsively I decided to take Dr. Frank's place.

Everybody opposed my decision—my friends, my colleagues, and even the almighty Superintendent of the City Hospitals. Why exchange the amenities of Vienna (in 1929 still the world's capital of music) for life in the woods? My colleagues spoke about my future career as a specialist, and the Superintendent, who was a great anatomist and also the Health Minister of Vienna, expressed his strong feeling that doctors who had been trained under his supervision should become pillars of socio-medical planning. Still, I decided to give country practice at least a trial. I compromised; I asked for a half year's leave of absence.

When I talked to my friends enthusiastically about the beauty of Burgenland and the enormous services a doctor can perform for country people, they said I was running after a childhood dream. Was it really true? I recalled Dr. Frank's house in the center of town—a spacious two-story building, painted egg yellow and built around a large courtyard shaded by walnut trees. The windowsills were filled with pots of geraniums. Patients lined up all day in the courtyard—Dr. Frank did not believe in waiting rooms. The doctor's mysterious office, into which I sometimes dared to peek, smelled of alcohol, iodine, and dust. It was frugally furnished with a table that served as a desk, two chairs, and a rickety examining table. An old cabinet containing a few instruments stood in a corner.

Dr. Frank was a slight man, with a comfortable paunch and a face that seldom smiled. I was always happy when he invited me to accompany him on his house calls. He would sit relaxed on the back seat of his carriage, in winter enveloped in a mighty fur coat. It was difficult territory—from valleys to mountaintops, one house many kilometres from another. Still, Dr. Frank said, he would not exchange his practice with that of a *Nichtstuer* doctor in a city. I enjoyed those excursions tremendously. When the snow melted, the whole countryside was saturated with green. Fruit trees blossomed into red, yellow, pink. Soon they would carry apples, pears, apricots, plums. Strawberries grew as big as children's fists. And, of course, there were vineyards as far as the eye could see. High on a mountaintop stood the medieval castle of the Duke of Esterhazy, and around it a virgin forest—chestnut trees and hunting territory.

As a medical student, I continued to visit the old doctor, but then I saw more than the countryside. There was work at hand for a country doctor. Sicknesses flourished that are all but extinct today. The whole territory was ridden with diphtheria (I can hardly believe it when a young doctor nowadays tells me that he has never seen one single case of diphtheria); typhoid fever was endemic, kept alive by contaminated wells; every third person had tuberculosis. Dr. Frank applied splints and plaster casts without X-ray diagnosis. When I remarked on this once, he looked indignant and snapped, "D'you see more crippled people here than in your famous Vienna?"

After Dr. Frank's death, I travelled down to Mattersburg to visit Frau Frank. I thought of renting Dr. Frank's old office and a couple of rooms in the spacious yellow house, but Frau Frank told me reluctantly that she preferred to live her remaining years alone in the house. I walked street after street, looking for suitable quarters in which to set up my practice. The ghetto had not changed since I was in Mattersburg almost ten years before—it had probably remained unchanged for centuries—but among the many peasant buildings in the main square I discovered a two-story building with a grocery store on the first floor and an apartment above. It was a modern apartment by Mattersburg standards, and I took it at once, paying four months' rent in advance.

The day my black nameplate, lettered in gold, was nailed on the entrance door, snow fell mixed with icy rain, but my heart felt as if it were spring. Upstairs, I had divided the apartment into office and living quarters. The office was equipped with the most modern tools and instruments, which I had arranged neatly in gray cabinets, and in a corner stood my X-ray machine. It was certainly the only one in a Burgenland doctor's office. Out in front of the building waited my little Opel-Steyr, which I had bought on the installment plan, like everything else. I was ready to receive patients and to make house calls.

No one came on the first day, or the day after. That was nothing, I thought—people must be given time to learn about the arrival of a new doctor; and after office hours I made my introductory calls on the notables in town: the priest, the rabbi, the superintendent of the school. But the doorbell didn't ring the third day, or on the fourth or fifth day, either. I drove up the hills, where snow had already settled on the tall fir trees. At night, I ate dinner alone in the inn and walked home through pitch-dark streets without meeting a living soul. Until midnight, when the Vienna radio stopped broadcasting, I listened to music.

Exactly one week after I had begun practicing, I was called to the house of my first patient. Her name was Sonnenschein, and she lived on a hill in the last building of the ghetto. I can still see that little figure with its birdlike face sitting up in bed, wrapped in several blankets. She had a metastatic breast cancer, and I noted morphine ampules at the bedside table. When I opened my bag and took out a syringe, she clutched the blankets to her. "Please, don't hurt me, Herr Doktor," she said.

I gave her the injection.

She took a deep breath. "It did not hurt much," she said. "No more than when Dr. Frank gave me the needle."

"Why should it hurt you more?" I said.

"Because people say that you're new. . . ."

I thought, Now at least the Jewish community will know that I don't murder people. There was a community of four hundred Jewish people in Mattersburg in my time, and I was counting on them in the first place when I settled there. A Jewish and a Gentile doctor in town was an age-old tradition. But many Gentiles preferred the Jewish physician. I recalled the large number of peasants waiting in Dr. Frank's courtyard.

My second patient came from the Gentile community, soon after Frau Sonnenschein called me. It was on a Sunday morning that my doorbell rang for the first time. I looked out the window and saw a young hunter helping an older one down from a peasant cart. The older man was pale and perspiring, his left arm in a sling; blood trickled through a dressing that had been clumsily applied. Arriving in my treatment room, he collapsed, and we carried him to the couch. His escort gave the history. The patient was the chief gamekeeper of the Duke's estate, and he had been injured when a gentleman-hunter's rifle went off accidentally. I cut open the dressing, discovered the source of bleeding—a minor artery—quickly ligated it, and closed the wound with a few stitches. Then I removed some grains of shot that had lodged under the skin.

Meanwhile, the patient revived, and asked for water. "Wine would be better," he said, smacking. His face regained its natural complexion—freckled from forehead to chin. With his healthy hand he brushed his close-cropped, flaming-red hair, then put on his hunter's cap, adorned with a long feather. "My name is Ferdl," he said, and shook my hand. "I was Dr. Frank's patient all my life, and I'm happy to meet his successor. I have confidence in Jewish doctors."

He must have spoken kindly about the new doctor's ability, because the following day two patients arrived from Neustift an der Rosalia, the village in which Ferdl lived, and one week later, when he arrived to have the stitches removed, I had treated a dozen patients.

I told him that his wound had healed fast.

"Hound's bones heal fast," he said, quoting an old proverb. He smiled broadly, showing healthy teeth, with one front tooth missing. He told me he had lost it on the Italian front, where in a hand-to-hand fight it was knocked out by an enemy's gun barrel. He asked me whether I was interested in rifle practice, and when I said yes he invited me to the castle court, where there was a rifle range.

The next day, a young peasant from Ferdl's village came to my office, accompanied by his wife. He had fallen from a tree and was caught by a strong branch, which had saved his life, he told me. But he complained about pain in his abdomen. As I examined him, I felt a mass behind the umbilicus that grew in size by the second. It was not hard to make the diagnosis: a hematoma caused by internal hemorrhage. I advised immediate hospitalization.

"But, Herr Doktor, people die in hospitals, don't they?" he said.

"No," I said. "You must go immediately."

"Not for such a trifle," the man said.

"You must," I said. "You will die if you don't."

"If I must die, I'd rather die at home," he said, and his wife agreed.

In a few hours, he was dead.

It was a terrible shock to me. That only an hour's drive from one of the great medical centers such an incredible thing could occur! Two days later, I watched the funeral procession. The man's wife walked calmly behind the cof-

fin with other mourners. The veterans' band played funeral
marches—not badly.

That same afternoon, I drove up the serpentines to
Burg Forchtenstein. Snow had fallen the previous night,
but the courtyard was brushed clean. Ferdl received me
with a broad smile. The view from the watchtower into the
valley was superb. We practiced target shooting for more
than an hour. I was a good shot, but Ferdl was, of course,
much better. He enjoyed himself tremendously when he
hit the bull's-eye. Finally, we gave our rifles to the helper,
and Ferdl invited me to the wine cellar. There we sat down
around a rough, unpolished table, and Ferdl filled the
glasses.

"*Prosit*," he said. "To many happy shootings. You *are*
good!"

There was a long pause after we drank.

"I must talk to you, Herr Doktor," Ferdl said, scratch-
ing his neck.

"It was not my fault," I said. I had been wanting to
speak of the episode.

"What d'you mean, Herr Doktor?"

"That poor man . . . I'm sorry. . . . I tried my best."

"But he's dead—Mischka didn't want to go to the hospital. He would have died anyhow. It's something else I
want to talk to you about—your other patients. There are
complaints against you, and I'm sorry." Ferdl moved
uneasily on the bench. "You must understand, Herr Doktor—I know people around here. They liked the way they
were treated by Dr. Frank. Not much talking. He only
looked at them, and sometimes not even that. I myself
recall when my smaller girl got sick around midnight, and
I drove down to town. I rang the doctor's bell and the Frau
Doktor looked out the window. 'What's wrong, Ferdl?' she
said. 'My Mitzi cannot swallow and she's hot,' I said. 'Wait
a minute,' she said, and went back where I knew the bed-

room was. A little later, she was again at the window, and dropped down a prescription of the medicine she said the girl must take—one teaspoonful every three hours. I said good night and she closed the window. I woke up the pharmacist, who filled the prescription. After a day, the girl was all right."

Ferdl refilled our glasses. "Well," he continued, "you spend too much time with your patients. It's a waste of time. Often you put them behind that Roentgen machine. . . ."

"My fees are small."

"It's not the money. People have something else to do. And you make them uneasy."

As I drove back down the serpentines, I thought of my plans to bring a modern medical approach to the country —preventive medicine.

———

CHRISTMAS had passed and Frau Sonnenschein remained my only Jewish patient. On New Year's Day, a young man with a wide-brimmed hat and curls in front of his ears summoned me to the deputy rabbi's home. The deputy rabbi was dean of the local Talmudic school, which had a great reputation among Orthodox Jews far and wide. The boy who came to my office was one of his students. When I asked him what was wrong with the rabbi, he only shrugged.

I took my bag and followed the boy down Jew Street, where he stopped at a building across the street from the fifteenth-century synagogue. The door was Baroque, but the building was plain Renaissance—a narrow courtyard, loggias, brittle walls probably not painted for centuries. I went after the boy up a winding staircase, through a small foyer, and into a large room with whitewashed walls, a huge table in the middle, and two chairs facing each other. On one sat the man I had come to see.

His gray beard enveloped his whole face. He moved his body gently from side to side while he read from a big book with parchment pages. Apparently, he did not notice my presence, and I didn't want to disturb him. My escort left silently and I stood there for several minutes before the rabbi looked up. At once he extended his hand across the table. "Have you been here long?" he asked. "Why didn't you speak? Doctors have better things to do than watch an old man." Then he stood and began undressing himself, his kaftan first, followed by a couple of shirts. Soon he was standing naked before me.

I was puzzled. "What's wrong with you, Rabbi?" I asked.

"You are the doctor, aren't you?" he said mildly.

He was a skinny man—his ribs stood out—but otherwise he looked healthy. I examined his heart, listened to his lungs, took his blood pressure. He said, with a gesture, that I could skip examining his abdomen—his digestion was perfect. He had no hernia; his reflexes were normal, and so was his gait. I was ready to give an opinion. "There's nothing wrong with you, Rabbi," I said.

"Nothing?"

I looked into round, mellow eyes. I was thinking hard. He had flat feet—but could that be called a sickness?

"Any backache?" I said.

Instantly, he started to dress. With deliberation he buttoned his suspenders to his trousers, then put on his kaftan. He sat down. His thin lips, barely showing through the beard, parted in a smile. "You made the *right* diagnosis," he said finally.

I told him to get arch supports, and I put my stethoscope and blood-pressure machine into my bag. I was ready to leave.

"Can you spare a few additional minutes of your valuable time, Herr Doktor?" I heard him say.

"Yes, Rabbi," I said, and sat down.

"Good. I would like to talk with you. People get nearer to each other when they talk. . . . How do you like it in our little town? You were used to life in a big city."

"It's all right," I said.

"People are different in a little town—I would say a bit suspicious. Well, to make it short, they were used to Dr. Frank—fifty years is a long time. He was the way old men are—a bit morose, often impatient—but, all in all, *ein ganzer Mensch*. And a good diagnostician. When he gave the diagnosis, it sounded like a verdict." With pale fingers he twisted his beard into strands. "I hope I don't hurt your feelings if I ask you how old you are."

"Twenty-eight."

"Young. My mother used to say that a doctor was no good until he filled up a cemetery." He smiled. "But one hears nowadays that young doctors also know their business. Peasants from the villages who come to shop talk kindly about you. And now I can also."

I felt I had passed, once again, an exam. I started to rise to say goodbye.

His long arms stretched across the table and restrained me. "Only a few additional words, Herr Doktor. I hope one day you'll get married. I hope you marry a good Jewish girl. And then don't forget that we've two kosher butchers in town. And we hope you'll come to the synagogue—at least, for the High Holidays. Will you?"

I told him I would do my best. He shook my hand warmly.

M<small>Y</small> practice increased. There was no lack of work that winter—a bad season for flu and pneumonia. After my visit to the rabbi, Jewish patients came also. And my first patient, poor old Frau Sonnenschein, died in late January.

Around the beginning of February, Ferdl needed my services again. A young hunter summoned me at five in the morning. He tried to dissuade me from using my car, and when I still insisted he shrugged. "You'll see," he said. It had rained during the night, and the road was inundated in several places. Still, I managed to navigate my Opel-Steyr up the winding route that led to the castle. Here the principal road ended. Ferdl's house was a few kilometres beyond, but I didn't dare continue along the narrow, rutted path. While I deliberated, I heard the labored grinding of a horse and cart, and the tall figure of Ferdl emerged, topped by his hunter's hat.

On the way to his house, Ferdl told me that his wife had expectorated blood while lighting a fire on the kitchen hearth. She hadn't been feeling well since early the previous summer, coughed a great deal, and was losing weight. I listened and asked one or two questions. The symptoms, unless there were additional ones, easily suggested tuberculosis.

The car stopped at a neat house with a tiled roof, surrounded by chestnut trees on which still hung a few thorny chestnut shells, emptied of their contents. The air was crisp. One felt grateful for the sudden warmth of the kitchen. Two girls, twelve and thirteen, and an older girl of about twenty waited for us.

In the adjoining room, the patient lay under voluminous quilts. Her face was waxen, and the large eyes, so typical of tubercular patients, looked at me inquisitively. The examination proved it an advanced case.

Back in the kitchen, the family gathered around me. The two girls clearly resembled their parents, taking their blond hair and narrow, fragile faces from their mother and the freckles and curved noses from their father. The eldest girl, a beautiful creature, buxom, with deer-brown eyes, was the maid. Tears ran down Ferdl's cheeks when I gave my prognosis. "Are you sure, Herr Doktor?" he said, wiping the tears from the corners of his eyes with his fist.

I replied that I was but would confirm it by X-ray if his wife could be brought to my office. When, I asked, had she started coughing.

Ferdl thought for a while. "It was around the strawberry harvest—the end of June, about."

"Did you take her to the doctor?"

"Yes, to Dr. Frank, about the same time."

"And what did he say?"

"He examined her and said she had bronchitis. He gave her a prescription."

"And you never took her back?"

"Dr. Frank said it would get better—and I often renewed the prescription."

Biochemical drugs for treating tuberculosis were still two and a half decades away. There was a chance of pneumothorax and surgery if only one lung was infected. But the following day a chest X-ray of Ferdl's wife showed both lungs riddled with cavities. Ferdl—as expected—declined hospitalization, which I suggested to protect the young people from contagion. What was required, then, was only care. The young maid volunteered to look after the patient. She was the granddaughter of the local midwife, and she had been taught how to nurse, she said.

I needed a rest. Fortunately, I could take a day off and travel to Vienna. It was a slushy day, but walking in the streets of Vienna seemed heavenly. I went to my hospital and enjoyed the cleanliness, the serene atmosphere. In a joking way, I told my colleagues about life in the country. I said nothing about its frustrations; I still had to stick out three remaining months of my leave. I went to a concert and afterward sat in a café, breathing in deeply the air filled with tobacco smoke.

I started back to Mattersburg late that same day. When I arrived at my office, a cart was standing at the door. It belonged to a peasant, who told me that he had been waiting for several hours for my return. His little girl was sick, and his wife had instructed him that she wanted no other doctor. As soon as we set out, it started snowing again, and it took an hour to reach the top of the hill where he lived. The child had diphtheria. After treating her, I climbed back into the cart. The storm had developed into a blizzard, and the strong peasant horse struggled its way down the roads. By the time I arrived back to town, grayish daylight filtered through thick clouds. Vienna had faded in my memory.

WHEN Ferdl's wife died, in March, he retired from society, declining to drink wine with his neighbors, politely rejecting an invitation to visit me, and shunning the weekly target shooting in the courtyard. People saw him walking aimlessly in the woods, accompanied by his two beagles, which, with drooping ears, seemed to participate in their master's grief. Therefore, I was pleasantly surprised one day a month later to discover him among my patients in the waiting room. When his turn came, he insisted upon being last. I was puzzled.

He entered my office, nervously fumbling with his cap,

and peered back into the waiting room before I closed the door. "Are you sure, Herr Doktor, that no one can overhear?" he said anxiously.

I reassured him.

He took a deep breath, then wiped his brow with a large red handkerchief. "She seemed such a good girl," he began.

"Who?"

"Resl, our maid."

"What's wrong?"

Ferdl sighed. "She's expecting a baby—and she claims it's mine." He slumped into a chair and buried his head in his large hands.

I tried hard not to laugh at his classic gesture of despair. The young girl had made a favorable impression on me. She was good to the dying woman and seemed to be on the best of terms with the two daughters. "Come, now," I said, patting him on the back. "Congratulations are in order."

"No," he said. "It's not mine." He stood up and began to pace the room. "Her father and I were on the Italian front. He died. When I came home after the war, I heard that his wife had also died, of Spanish influenza, and their girl—she was then about eight—had been taken by her grandmother. Have you ever met Frau Handler, her grandmother? Well, you will one day. She must be close to ninety, but she still attends to her work as a midwife. Once, the town council thought it was time to replace her with a younger woman. They found one who had just graduated from the midwife school in Vienna. She took the job, but she wasn't lucky. The first two children she delivered died during birth. People said that while the women were in labor they saw Resl's grandmother hobbling around their houses, and some claim they even saw her riding on a broom. I don't believe such nonsense, do you? Well, at any rate, the young midwife was fired, and the old

woman took over again—people wanted to play safe. Then
last summer when my wife became too weak to do the
household chores and tend the garden, we looked for a
maid. Frau Handler came with her granddaughter. She
said life was hard, and she kept talking about my friendship
with her dead son. You know how old women carry
on. . . ."

I nodded.

"I never liked that woman," he said. "She has been a
gossip all her life, cutting people to pieces. But that day she
talked and talked, and finally I gave in. And now I am the
victim."

"But if you are not the father, why worry?"

"Because already everybody has heard the news. Even
the most reverend Herr Pfarrer congratulated me this
morning when I was in the church."

"Look, Ferdl," I said, "I'm a doctor. I treat illnesses,
patients. What can I do about gossip?"

"First, let me tell you what happened," he said. "After
my wife died, I sent Resl home to her grandmother. I
thought that my two daughters could keep house themselves. The girl left, apparently in good spirits. And then
a few days later when I came home one afternoon, I found
the old midwife sitting at the kitchen table. As soon as I
entered, she got up and hobbled over to me. 'Congratulations, Ferdl,' she said. She all but embraced me. 'Resl is
pregnant.' I told her I knew it. I didn't pay much attention.
Pregnancy out of wedlock is nothing new among these
country girls. I still didn't know what she wanted from me.
Wasn't Resl pregnant when she left my house, she asked.
I said, was I the only man in the world? And so one word
led to another, and finally I told her to get out. Later, I was
sorry; after all, she was an old woman. But she really made
me angry."

"Then?"

"I didn't hear anything more until a few days ago. Suddenly people began to hint at things, and finally the gossip was right out in the open. She did a good job—that witch." Ferdl sank into a chair. I worried about the cap with the long feather, which he twisted in his hands.

"Believe me," I said, "you have the sympathy of another man. But I don't know what I can do."

"You can do everything, Herr Doktor. I remember a case of a pregnant girl in town. She and her mother accused a man, and he denied it. The man went to Dr. Frank. He called the two scoundrels to his office. And after they came out they said they had lied. Dr. Frank was a great man. He helped everybody. Talk to Frau Handler."

Three days later, I spotted Frau Handler in my waiting room. It was not hard to recognize her. When she sat down in the chair facing me, I found a striking resemblance between her eyes and the deer-brown eyes of her granddaughter. The eyes alone retained a spark of youth. "Do you know who I am?" she asked.

I said that I did.

"Then you probably know the reason for my coming."

"Well," I said evasively, "you're the midwife, aren't you?"

She nodded. "Do you know Ferdl, the gamekeeper?"

"He is my patient," I said.

"Well then, you can be of great help. Ferdl is shirking his duties as the father of a newborn child."

"It was born?" I asked in surprise.

"This morning at four. A little boy—four kilograms—with fire-red hair, and a lot of it. Even freckles!"

"Congratulations."

"*Danke schön.*" The old woman played nervously with the wings of her kerchief. "Herr Doktor, I came here to ask you to persuade the villain of his duty."

"But Ferdl denies it flatly," I said.

"Aha!" She laughed. "A fine gentleman! First he leads a good, innocent girl astray, then he says, 'Not me—somebody else.' "

"And what does Resl say?"

"Resl says nothing. You can talk and plead and shout, and that stupid goose simply cries."

"Then how can you prove it?"

"How? Very simple. Look at the baby. The image of his father—the hair and the big hands. Listen, do you know who delivered Ferdl himself? I did, and I remember every child I ever delivered. I remember Ferdl—the hair and the hands. When I saw those hands, I said that he would become a hunter one day, and a good one."

Next morning, I travelled up to the midwife's house. Like Ferdl's, it was in the forest, but nearer to the castle. It was a cottage, with a tiny garden around it; smoke wafted from the chimney. Twenty-four hours after delivery, Resl was already on her feet, and when I entered the house she was bathing her baby happily. When I looked at the baby, I was thunderstruck—it *was* the image of Ferdl.

Resl lifted up the homely creature. "Isn't it wonderful?" she said.

The old woman was hobbling around, pouring water into a large pail on the hearth. She turned to Resl. "Now speak up," she said.

At once, Resl began to cry.

"Stupid goose," Frau Handler said. "You see, she is hopeless. What can be done? She cannot live in shame and raise a child without a father. You must speak with that *Bösewicht*, Herr Doktor."

I threw up my hands. "I'll see what I can do."

"*Bitte*," she said, and as I left she muttered, "Why is good old Dr. Frank not here?"

I drove up to Ferdl's house. He was cleaning his rifle while the beagles stood and watched with boredom. He expressed surprise at seeing me at such an early hour. I usually made house calls late in the afternoon.

"I just visited Resl," I said. "She has a baby—a little boy."

"So?" he said, without interrupting his work.

"The baby has red hair and large hands."

He looked up. "What do you imply?" he said sharply.

"It speaks for itself," I said.

"Am I the only man with red hair and big hands?" He shook his head. "You'd better have a glass of wine, Herr Doktor. I think the old woman has bewitched you."

THE arrival of the little red-haired boy was the topic of conversation everywhere I went. Women in black kerchiefs leaned out of their windows to question me; men stopped me on the street. Public opinion was convinced of the hunter's paternity—and so was I.

I was not surprised, therefore, when the rabbi called me to his house one day and didn't make a move to undress. "What's going on in that Ferdl affair?" he said, stroking his beard.

"I don't know any more than you, Rabbi," I said.

"Did you appeal to his conscience?"

I looked with astonishment at the old man. "Wouldn't it be the duty of a clergyman to do that?" I said. "I am a doctor."

The rabbi shook his head. "No, Herr Doktor, not only the clergyman. Dr. Frank—may he rest in peace—would have spoken up, and would have acted already. I don't say that in every case the doctor has to put in a word. We Jews shouldn't meddle in the affairs of our Gentile neighbors. But this case is—I hear from everywhere—evidently in favor of poor Frau Handler's granddaughter. And Frau Handler is the midwife. She has helped everyone, Jew and Gentile alike. Isn't it our duty to help her when she's in need?"

"How?"

"You should not give up. We Jews know best what it means to suffer injustice. Herr Doktor, you must try once more."

"But what must I do?"

"People believe in their doctor. Even our laws say"—he wagged his right index finger toward the big book on the table—"that a doctor equals the wise men in our history. He can help if he will. People look up to him as a father. Persuade that bad man he is wrong."

By the time I left the rabbi, I was quite weary of my involvement with this problem in human relations. I met Ferdl when I was making house calls later. He lifted his hat politely but didn't stop, ignoring my move to speak.

My leave of absence neared its end, and I decided to resume my residency in Vienna. I knew that I must catch up with things I had missed since leaving the hospital. Practice slowed down a bit after the winter months, and I enrolled in a postgraduate course in hematology, which had developed into a major area of modern medicine. The research work of Dr. Landsteiner, a Viennese doctor who that same year received the Nobel Prize for discovering the so-called blood groups, had begun thirty years earlier, and we had already learned in medical school about these four blood groups: A, B, AB, and O. The large majority of Western people belonged to group O, and the rest were divided between A and B. Only five per cent belonged to group AB.

It was an unusually hot day in May when I attended the first session of the course. After the lecturer had given basic information about recent advances in hematology, he turned to complicated theoretical interpretations. The room was steaming, and the numbers and letters on the blackboard seemed to fuse. But then suddenly I heard something of which I recall even now, forty years later, almost every word. "There is a by-product of the research into the blood-group field—although it belongs more in the province of legal medicine," said the lecturer, Dr. Halter, a thin, slightly bent middle-aged man with a spry mustache. "Paternity can be *disproved* if the child and the accused father do not belong to the same blood grouping."

I could hardly wait until the lecture finished. I followed Dr. Halter into his laboratory and told him about Ferdl, Resl, and the midwife.

"*Aber, Herr Kollege*," he said after I concluded my story, "everything is still part of a research program. It would never stand a chance in court—and I wouldn't be part of it." He shook his head.

"It wouldn't go to court. Word of honor."

"Don't look for trouble," he said.

I kept on talking, and finally Dr. Halter took a deep breath.

"All right," he said. "Bring samples of the blood of the child and that hunter, although I doubt that he will submit. But now leave me alone."

The following morning at six, I was at the midwife's house.

"Well," she said, "has he owned up to it?"

"No," I said, "but we'll try something else." We settled down at the kitchen table, and I proceeded as simply as possible to explain the theory of the blood groups to her. Those young brown eyes were fixed on me. "Now, you see," I said, "if the baby belongs to one of those groups and Ferdl another, then it is not his baby."

"And whose is it?" she asked defiantly.

"Let me finish. Even if they should have the same group —Well, it is not positive evidence, I must warn you." I cleared my throat and began a theoretical explanation. The more I progressed, the more I became confused. I was ready to give up when the old woman interrupted me.

"Look, Herr Doktor," she said. "I'm a midwife for sixty-five years. When we started, we didn't wash our hands with soap and chlor water before we helped to deliver. Many, many mothers died of fever. But then we heard of that doctor—Semmelweis—and we were told to wash our hands. I didn't understand, but I did it. I don't understand what those blood groups mean, but I believe in science."

She assisted me when I drew 5 cc.s from the baby's arm.

I went on to Ferdl's house.

Ferdl listened to my explanation without interruption. After I finished, he shook his head, as though dazed. "I can hit a hare from three hundred metres, and the bull's-eye ten times in a row, as you know, but I don't understand one single word you have said. But you must know what you are talking about. Go ahead."

I packed the two vials into my bag and set out for Vienna.

Dr. Halter typed the baby's blood first. It belonged to the rarest group—AB. I held my breath when Dr. Halter typed Ferdl's blood. It, too, was AB. I felt jubilant.

Dr. Halter bit his mustache. "It's still only a probability, remember," he warned me.

I made the trip home in half an hour less than usual, and drove straight to Ferdl. "The baby and you belong to the same blood group," I said sternly.

Ferdl glanced around him, and his eyes met mine. He shrugged. "Well," he said. "Science must know best."

THAT evening, a strange procession came to my office: a dozen Jewish firemen in uniform. Although the Jewish community was an integral part of the town, the fire department of the Jews had retained its medieval status of autonomy. This fire department had a great reputation among Jews and Gentiles alike. If fire broke out even in remote villages, the Jewish firemen could be counted on to arrive first. The firemen informed me that in a special meeting I had been elected president of the fire department. I answered that I felt honored, but my knowledge of fighting fire was negligible. They assured me that no special knowledge on my part was required. I consented, thinking that my position would be purely honorary.

A fortnight later, I slept, unaware that the fire alarm had sounded. I was wakened by voices in the street and the rattling of a fire engine very near. When I looked out the window, I saw my firemen standing around their engine.

"Hurry up, Herr Doktor," they shouted. "There's a fire in Antau"—a village fifteen kilometres away. A minute later, a helmet was squeezed over my head, and I was helped into a fireman's blouse. The boots I pulled up while I was sitting in the engine.

Again the Jewish firemen were first!

Since my leave of absence from the hospital was soon to expire, I travelled to Vienna to request from my chief another half year of leave. "Can I abandon my fire department?" I ended my speech.

My request was granted, but I never returned to Vienna. I stayed in Mattersburg another eight years, until I was driven out by the Nazis.

The Red Bicycle

W E were living in Mattersburg at the time of the
Anschluss—my wife, Maria; Peter, our six-year-old
son; and I. In the days that followed, the doors and
windows of the fourteenth-century synagogue were
smashed, homes were looted, and the Jewish male population was herded into the county jail. I, the town doctor,
was not spared. But through some unaccountable over-
sight, Peter's bicycle was not confiscated, as all the other
Jewish property was.

Peter had received his bicycle only a few months before, on his birthday. I had bought the smallest one available in a Vienna department store, but even it had proved
too big for Peter's short legs. Somehow, though, he had
learned to turn the pedals and maneuver while sitting directly on the bar of the frame. It was sensational for a little

boy to have a bicycle in Mattersburg, and he would be watched by scores of children as he rode around Main Square.

Peter's friends took part in the proceedings that followed the Anschluss. They paraded, sang the "Horst Wessel Lied," and smashed Jewish windows. But then they tired of playing with their elders and returned to their own games. Those were balmy, sunny days—the warmest spring in history. The ground was dry, ideal for bicycle riding. Only once did a little girl—blond, freckle-faced Mitzi—ask whether a Jewish boy could still own a bicycle. The other children told her it was all right; the announcement said that Jewish children were not permitted to enter parks and/or sit on benches (the park of Mattersburg had only one bench, anyhow), but there was nothing in it about bicycles. So Peter visited me often in jail, wheeling his bicycle right into the courtyard. That bicycle was the source of our unwarranted optimism about the intentions of the Nazis toward the Jews.

One day, I was released from jail on condition that I leave Nazi territory within two weeks. We moved hurriedly to Vienna, and the bicycle went along. In Vienna, I succeeded in getting visas for the three of us to go to France. We were permitted to take only twenty marks out of the country. Since everything we possessed had been confiscated, there was not much more we could have taken even if it had been permitted. I sold the bicycle for thirty marks and with that money bought three pairs of shoes—a pair apiece. Peter was not happy about the transaction, but I promised him that one day he would own another bicycle.

We did not remain long in France. Almost at once, I received an appointment as a colonial physician on the Ivory Coast, and I served there for a year, until a mild attack of tuberculosis made it necessary for me to return to Europe. We went to Paris. It was impossible to get a license to practice in France, so I did all kinds of odd jobs. Somehow we survived. Then the war broke out. We did not feel its effect at first, but in May, 1940, the Germans smashed through Belgium into France, and one day airplanes with swastikas on their wings flew over the roofs of the city. Despite official assurances that the Germans would never appear, we decided to take no chances. On the tenth of July, early in the morning, we left our apartment on the Boulevard Richard-Lenoir, near the Place de la Bastille, with only as many of our belongings as we could pack into Peter's rucksack and carrying his pet parrot in a cage. The Métro was no longer running, and no taxis were available. We walked all the way to the Gare d'Orléans, the point of departure for the southwest.

Beyond Pont Solférino, we found the streets leading to the station clogged with people—everyone laden with suitcases, packages, bundles of food, pots and pans, even mattresses. Before we knew it, we were caught in the stamping, jostling mass, which seemed to be moving steadily but getting nowhere. Hours passed, and we made hardly any progress toward the station entrance. It was a terribly hot day, and there was, of course, no water available. Peter's parrot became agitated, and its cries mingled with the complaints of the children. Many people had given up the idea of getting into the station, but it was impossible to get free of the crowd. Suddenly there was a surge forward, and we found ourselves in the station. I can't explain how it happened, but there we were; we could breathe once more, and we were practically alone. There weren't more than half a dozen people in that large place. From outside came shouts of "No trains! No trains are running!" And then another stroke of luck—a train. Cars rolled past, paused, jolted, started ahead again, and stopped.

We scrambled aboard, into an empty compartment. No one else followed. We had no idea where the train was heading or, indeed, whether it would move again. A man in uniform, with a gun—apparently a *réserviste*—stuck his head in the compartment. Peter asked for water for his parrot, which lay prostrate on the floor of its cage. The man smiled, disappeared, and soon returned with a glass of water. He staggered; he was happily drunk. The bird was quickly revived, and jumped up and down. With a jolt, the train started to move. "Where is the train going?" I asked the man, who presumably was the guard.

"Who knows?" he said.

The train seemed to change its mind half a dozen times an hour—steaming forward at top speed, screeching to a sudden stop, backing up, halting, shuddering, then bolting off again.

"What the devil is going on?" I asked the *réserviste*, who had decided to stay with us and had taken a seat. He was asleep. The countryside hurtled past the window. We were well beyond Paris, and as far as I could gauge from the sun's position, going south. Maria and Peter were asleep, too, and so was the parrot, its cage covered by a towel.

Sometime during the night, I dozed. A hand shook me awake, and a voice said, "Last stop." In the dim light, I saw a fat, bearded face—a sweating giant in oil-stained clothes, obviously the engineer.

I looked at my watch; it was one o'clock. "Where are we?" I asked.

"Montauban!" he roared. He gave the sleeping soldier a cuff on the face and left.

Where was Montauban, I wondered, staring out the window at the railroad station. I woke up Maria and Peter, and we opened the heavy door of the coach and clambered out. We were the only ones to emerge from the train. For all I know, we were the only passengers on that strange journey. We walked the length of the platform, then down a street in the direction of a distant light. As we drew closer, we could see that it illuminated a battered sign: "Hôtel d'Andorra." We had to pick our way through sleeping figures on the sidewalk—refugees who had arrived before us. At the inn, I rang the bell several times but got no response. We settled among the others on the sidewalk. I sat leaning against the wall. Peter fell asleep with his head on my lap, and Maria rested against my shoulder.

Shortly before dawn, I heard someone call for a doctor. A woman in a long blue dressing gown stood in the open door of the inn. I thought I must be hallucinating, but when she said again, "A doctor—get a doctor," I stood up. I felt my breast pocket, where I always kept my stethoscope; it was there. In my jacket pockets, I ran my fingers over the few medical supplies I had brought with me—a syringe, some ampules of digitalis and caffeine, and a small box of assorted pills. "I'm a doctor," I said.

"Come with me, please," the woman said.

She ran up two flights of stairs, and I followed her. We entered a room where a tousle-haired little girl, about eight years old, was sitting up in bed. At that moment, the light went off. "There isn't enough electric current in town," the woman said. The little girl started to cry, and the woman went off to fetch candles. "Are you really a doctor?" she asked when she returned, a few minutes later.

I looked at my rumpled clothes; then I took out my stethoscope.

"Thank God," she said. "There doesn't seem to be a doctor left in Montauban." She had changed into a heavy black dress, drawn in at the waist by a belt, from which hung a collection of keys. She was unquestionably the innkeeper.

The little girl's face was flushed, and the left half was swollen. I diagnosed the trouble as mumps and reassured the woman, whose name I now learned was Mme. Juin. The little girl, Gisèle, was her daughter.

"You arrived during the night?" Mme. Juin asked.

"Yes," I said. "By train—from Paris."

"But how? The trains are not running, except for the military. I heard it on the radio. Colonial troops are being moved from Marseille and Bordeaux to stem the advance of the Boches."

I told her about the ghost train, and about Maria and Peter out on the street. She urged me to get them at once. When I brought them in, we found a table set with bread, butter, and preserves, and presently Mme. Juin came in from the kitchen with steaming coffee.

She was a tall woman, with a pale complexion, dark eyes, and a slightly curved nose—very handsome. (In the South of France, nearby Spain has had a strong biological impact.) She spoke very fast, with that patois of the Midi that emphasizes the last syllable of each word. While she moved nervously around the room, she stroked her smooth auburn hair. At one point, she stopped to indicate a photograph of her husband that hung on the wall—a smiling young man in uniform. He was somewhere on the Maginot Line. I did not tell her the Line had been erased.

"We must get you settled," she said. "I'm sorry that I have no more rooms, but we shall find places for you somewhere." Over our protests, she decided that we should have her bedroom; she would sleep on a couch in Gisèle's room. Another couch would be moved into our room for Peter.

Gisèle recovered after a week, but I did not lack for patients. Mme. Juin had sent me to see Mme. Berton, wife of the local police captain, who was suffering from worry over a sick child, stricken with measles, I discovered. Mme. Berton sent me to others. Flouting regulations, Captain Berton issued me a certificate—probably worthless—permitting me to practice, and soon I was making many house calls. Few people were able to pay, however, and the sum of money we had brought from Paris was dwindling. We paid for our lodgings, against the wishes of Mme. Juin, and our food, we bought a little clothing, and there was nothing left for the slightest luxury.

Therefore, I was greatly disturbed to have Peter burst in one day after lunch, panting and so excited he could hardly speak. On the Place Nationale, he said, under the arcades, in front of the butcher shop, there was a long line of people. "And there's a man there in the line who has a *bicycle* he wants to sell! And he wants only five hundred francs!" The man's name was Campuneaud, and the bicycle had excellent brakes. "It stops—I rode it around the square, twice, and it stops just like that!"

Ever since our departure from Austria, Peter had been looking wistfully at bicycles. In Africa, the son of our Syrian grocer owned a bicycle for delivery. He let Peter ride around on it after school, and in this way the bicycle problem had been temporarily solved. In Paris, the parrot had occupied his mind. But now . . .

"It's red, Daddy. Did I tell you it was red?"

"Well," I said, patting his head. "Someday, when we can afford a new bicycle, you can choose any color you want."

"You promised. All you ever do is promise."

"Someday, Peter."

"Don't keep repeating that, please," Maria said.

"But it's out of the question now. *You* must know better."

Mme. Juin and Gisèle appeared in the doorway. They had been listening. "What a shame," said Mme. Juin. "Every boy should have a bicycle."

"Mme. Juin, we can't afford it. Don't you understand?"

She touched the heavy purse fastened on her belt, next to the keys. "But, Doctor, you'll be able to pay it back soon."

"No. It's out of the question."

Gisèle cried, and Peter was gloomy. I surveyed the group confronting me and realized that I had, at least, to investigate.

———

NEXT morning, I went with Peter to the Place Nationale, and there indeed, in the waiting line before the Charcuterie Fouchon, was M. Campuneaud with the red bicycle. M. Campuneaud personified the defeat of France. He wore a rumpled fatigue jacket with all the buttons missing; his shoes were torn and fastened with string. It was hard to tell whether he was a soldier or a civilian, because soldiers running away from their outfits hastily acquired civilian clothes. He was a sorry sight, but Peter gazed at him worshipfully; he could have been the President of the Republic. M. Campuneaud greeted us with a broad smile, an energetic handshake, and a sales talk. The price of the bicycle, he said, was "a mere five hundred francs, and a bargain not to be matched anywhere."

I fingered the few bills in my pocket—perhaps thirty francs all told.

M. Campuneaud propped the bicycle against a pillar and explained how attached to it he was.

"I really don't wish to sell it," he said. "I came with it all the way from Paris. But my family will arrive in Montauban at any time, and I need the money."

"We're short of money, too," Peter confessed.

"Ah, yes," said M. Campuneaud, shaking his head.

"Do you have any diseases, Monsieur?" asked Peter.

"Diseases? I feel fine."

"My father is a doctor," said Peter. "If you had a disease of some kind—any kind—he could cure it."

"That's enough, Peter!" I said. Some of my patients had been offering fruit, eggs, a piece of cheese, or a bottle of wine, and, of course, Peter knew it.

"I'm sorry," said M. Campuneaud. "I have not been sick for ten years, outside of a touch of influenza. Ten years ago, however, I had a sore back. Right here." He twisted around to demonstrate.

"My father could cure your back," Peter said.

"Come, Peter," I said. "We must go along."

"Wait, Doctor," M. Campuneaud said. "I wonder, would you be willing to pay three hundred fifty francs, perhaps?" He patted the bicycle.

"Two hundred," I heard myself saying.

"Two hundred," Peter echoed.

"It is yours," said M. Campuneaud, beaming at Peter.

As buyer, I was expected to buy drinks, so the three of us walked to the corner *bistro*, Peter wheeling the bicycle. Over wine, M. Campuneaud began to make a better impression on me. He was a workingman from a Paris suburb. He told me about his family and explained how as the Boches came nearer and nearer he had decided to flee.

We finished our drinks and stepped outside. Peter and the bicycle had disappeared.

"He's only trying it out," said M. Campuneaud. "He'll be back soon. If we had a bite to eat, he would probably return before we finished our coffee."

This seemed reasonable, and I went with him into a neighboring restaurant. I ordered a meal, but M. Campuneaud had changed his mind about eating and asked only for wine. He drank a bit too much and before long began to sing, joined by a group of soldiers at the next table. Between songs, there was a discussion of the war. Some thought that the British should be left to shift for themselves, others that France should follow the appeal of General de Gaulle in his radio address from London. M. Campuneaud, now quite violent, was for continuation of the war from abroad. "*Vive de Gaulle!*" he shouted, and more wine was ordered.

I began going out every few minutes to see if Peter had returned. M. Campuneaud suggested we go back to the *bistro*. There, after another drink, his head sank to the table; he was sound asleep. I walked to the Hôtel d'Andorra and, carefully avoiding Maria, asked Mme. Juin for the use of her car—an aged, tiny Renault. For nearly two hours, I drove, returning now and again to the *bistro;* still there was no trace of the boy. Finally, I had no choice but to notify the police—and Maria.

Captain Berton promised to do everything in his power, but this was not reassurance enough for Maria, who was near collapse. I was sitting with her about nine that evening, trying to quiet her, when a *garde mobile* appeared at the door of the inn, the red bicycle at his side. At first, he seemed to be alone, but then he stepped aside, revealing Peter. "This is your son?" he asked.

"Yes," I said.

"We found him in the country—twelve, fifteen kilometres from the city. He had stolen this bicycle. A bad boy."

"I didn't steal it!" Peter cried. "I was going to see Léon." Léon was a schoolmate, who lived with his parents on a farm. "I thought maybe we would not have the money to buy the bicycle, and I wanted to show it to Léon. I was resting at the side of the road when *he* and another *garde mobile* stopped me and asked me all those questions."

"Yes, a big question," said the officer. "Whose bicycle is this? Look, here at the mark. It is government property. It has been stolen."

"I *told* them we were buying it."

"Is that true?" the officer asked me.

"Yes," I said.

The officer scratched his head. "The boy should be punished," he said. "We have nothing but trouble here now, with all these refugees."

Mme. Juin came into the hall. "What's all this!" she demanded. She reached a quick conclusion, which was that the *garde mobile* was making an impossible nuisance of himself, and she told him so.

"But, Monique," he said.

"Don't you call me Monique, you shirker! My husband is fighting for *la patrie*. And where are you?"

The *garde mobile* departed. I suddenly remembered M. Campuneaud, borrowed two hundred francs from Mme. Juin, and ran to the *bistro*. The *patron* told me that the man had gone some time ago.

———————

It was unheard of for a young boy to have a bicycle in Montauban, and, as in Mattersburg, it gave Peter a special status. But for Maria and me the bicycle became a new source of anxiety. Montauban was an old Huguenot town, with twisting, medieval streets, built on hilly terrain. Peter would ride with lightning speed, stepping on the brakes at the very last second as a jeep, lorry, or some other military vehicle came laboring toward him up a hill. When he rode around the Place Nationale, people under the arcades would cross themselves. The streets resounded with the excited yells of children, watching Peter or waiting to take turns riding.

One day, we went to Mme. Juin's room, and there she sat, pale and stroking her hair. A telegram lay on the table; on the wall the picture of her husband was covered by a black veil. She sat, head down, for a moment; then she straightened up. "We must not live in the past," she said.

The winter of 1940-41 was bitterly cold—one of the coldest in the history of the Midi. Icicles as tall as a man hung from the eaves, and snow driven by heavy winds piled in drifts high above the first-floor window sills. Fuel became scarce, then almost nonexistent, and Peter began making daily trips on his bicycle to the outskirts of town for firewood. Food also became scarce, although we fared better than many. Mme. Juin owned a few acres in a neighboring village; her tenant there paid part of his rent in milk and eggs, which he brought to town twice a week. These were generously shared with us, the milk being reserved for the children. Mme. Juin's sister, who lived on a large farm, came with her family to visit occasionally and always brought along several chickens and preserved fruit. For days at a time, however, there would be nothing but a very pale, watery soup and, once a day, bread.

But cold and hunger were not the most important among our problems. By this time, the Vichy regime was zealously collaborating with the Nazis in Paris, rooting out refugees who had fled from German-occupied territories to the so-called unoccupied areas of France. This work was mostly in the hands of an auxiliary police force under the leadership of the notorious former member of the Paris municipal council, Doriot. Increasing numbers of jack-booted cops began showing up in Montauban, and, in addition, S.S. men—some in full uniform, others in disguise. It was only a question of time, as our friend the police captain told me, and as, indeed, I could well see for myself, until they got around to us. Where would we go now? Switzerland? Many had been caught trying to cross that border and had been packed off in prison trains bound for Germany. Spain? The border was closer, but even if one could cross it, what sort of haven was to be found in a country bossed by Hitler's friend and admirer? For countries overseas, there was the impossible matter of visas. By early spring, things had reached the point where we hardly dared show our faces outside. Every night, we expected the knock on the door.

One morning, a letter came for us from an international children's-aid organization with headquarters in Marseille and the United States. Arrangements had been made, it said, to evacuate from France the children of refugees who themselves had no hope of emigrating. All that was necessary was to make application; a ship was preparing for departure in two weeks.

Difficult as the decision was, we made it quickly. I filled out the application, and we prepared a story for Peter. He was to go first, we told him; we would be joining him soon. "*How* soon?" was his almost hourly question. As we attempted to answer him, any difficulties we had had until now seemed inconsequential. How soon indeed.

On the twenty-first of March, Maria's birthday, I called at the post office for *poste-restante* letters that might have arrived. There was a telegram. I concluded that it was a birthday greeting for Maria, and put it in my pocket. When I got back to the inn, I handed it to her. She opened it. It was from the Consul-General of the United States in Marseille, and it said that special emergency visas had been granted to all three of us by the Department of State.

In our joy and eagerness, we thought that all we had to do was pick up the visas, but it was not that simple. To pick up the visas, one had to go to Marseille. Foreigners from Nazi-occupied territories were permitted to travel in unoccupied France only if they possessed permits to leave the country—and although exit permits were given to those with overseas visas, boat tickets, and the approval of the German armistice commission, they were obtainable only in Vichy. Appearance before the armistice commission would mean just one thing for us: the Gestapo. There was no certain way out of the circle.

I decided to go to Marseille without authorization. The train was to leave at five in the morning. I was there on time, but at five-thirty the train still stood in the station, with more and more passengers boarding every minute. At six, a patrol of Doriot cops entered the front cars, to check identification papers. I went quickly to the rear of the train, got out, pushed through the crowd, and walked ahead to a car that had been checked. Finally, the train began to move. At Toulouse, where I had to change trains, passengers were directed to a checking desk, for another police inspection before entering the train for Marseille. No sly maneuver would do here; I decided to make a dash for it. I came close to bringing it off, too, and was just stepping into the train when a hand fell on my shoulder. It was a cop, dressed in the costume typical of the Doriot auxiliary police—half uniform and half civilian clothing. "Wait!" he commanded. "Let me see your papers." I fumbled for my wallet. He grabbed it from my hand and opened it. He took out a sheaf of papers and began going through them. He seemed to take special interest in one, and, leaning forward, I saw that it was my honorable discharge from the Colonial Service—something I had all but forgotten I possessed. "Mmmm," he said, reading and rereading. "Mmmm." Then, *"Merci bien!"*

When I reached Marseille, the American Consulate was closing for the day, with a long line still waiting in front of the door. The next morning, I made a point of being among the first in line. I produced the telegram, and the clerk, speaking in French after trying me in English, said, "Yes, you and your family will receive visas, but, according to regulations, only after you are able to show us tickets for a ship sailing from France."

Where could one find such a ship, I asked.

"I'm sorry," she said. "I really can't say. I'd like to help you, but . . . Good luck!"

That afternoon, I learned of a committee that was operating semi-legally in Marseille. Its head was Varian Fry, an American whose name at the time was being whispered among those whose lives were in imminent danger. No one was ready to say just what was going on, but the name Varian Fry was passed along as though it carried much importance. Without real hope, I went to the committee. I was told that the committee was trying to obtain a British Navy permit for a Vichy ship carrying refugees to pass through the blockade. Nobody would say anything more. To the vital question *when*, I received no reply. "Keep in touch with us" was all they would say.

I returned to Montauban, weakly encouraged. There I found an urgent message; I was to go at once to see Captain Berton, at police headquarters. When I arrived, he handed me a document. "This will make it easier, " he said. It was an official exit permit, signed by the Minister of Interior of the Vichy regime. "Just don't ask me questions," Captain Berton said. It was time for us to leave. Orders had come from Vichy to evacuate all Jewish refugees.

We began to pack our few things immediately—most of them fitted easily into Peter's old rucksack. Mme. Juin put together a package containing nearly all the food she had in her kitchen and insisted we take it with us. At four in the morning, we went out to climb into Mme. Juin's small car, with its coughing engine, its cracked windshield, and its paper-thin tires. It was a dreary departure, made no brighter by Mme. Juin's flood of tears as she took her place behind the wheel. Everyone was in the car but Peter. I looked out and saw him struggling with something in the half darkness. It was his bicycle, which he was trying to hoist up to the top of the car.

"No, Peter!" I shouted, getting out. "That's impossible. There is no room here, and there will be no room on the ship. You'll have to leave the bicycle here."

"Isn't there *some* way?" Maria asked.

"Please," I said to her. "Don't make it any harder."

"Oh dear, oh dear," Mme. Juin said.

"*Please*, Daddy."

The strain of waiting, the uncertainty, the sleepless nights had caught up with me. I had no more patience. "Put the bicycle down!" I said. "Come, get in the car. You can't take it."

"Oh, the poor child," Mme. Juin said.

"Peter loves his bicycle very much," said Gisèle.

"Couldn't you tie it on top of the car?" Maria asked.

"Daddy! I have to leave my parrot, but not my bicycle, too!"

I tied the bicycle onto the top of the car, thinking that we would take it only as far as the railroad station. There, surely, we would be forbidden to put it on the train. Someone else—some railroad official—could give the cruel, final command.

When we got to the station, I took the bicycle down, and Peter wheeled it along. We said our farewells to Mme. Juin and Gisèle and headed down the platform. To my amazement, no objection was raised as Peter—and the bicycle—preceded us into the car. The train was so crowded, the confusion so great, that nobody seemed to pay attention to anyone else. I noticed some Doriot cops, but they ignored us.

In Marseille, we waited four weeks, mostly in hiding, before the Varian Fry committee notified us that a freighter bound for Martinique would be leaving soon. Now, at last, we were given our American visas.

On the day of sailing, we walked to the pier, Peter wheeling his bicycle. I had made it clear to him, however, that the time had come when he would have to part with it, and I proved to be correct. A ship's officer explained that nothing not absolutely essential could be taken aboard; the ship was too crowded. But it was not a question of relinquishing the bicycle; it would be stored for him. The genial officer explained all this carefully, and Peter's anguish abated somewhat. He wrote his name and mine on a tag, which he affixed to the bicycle's handlebars. "You can send it to me when the war is over," Peter said.

"Oh, yes. *Yes!*" the officer assured him.

AFTER the conclusion of the war, in 1946, the French government set up a committee to arrange for the recovery of property abandoned during the great exodus. In New York that year, we received a questionnaire to fill out, requesting the places in France where we had left items of personal property, and a description of the items left. Maria and I focussed our attention on the apartment we had had in Paris, trying to recall precisely what had been abandoned there. We received no reply to the questionnaire for nine years. Then, in 1955, we had a letter. The Paris property had vanished, it seemed; there was no trace of it. But records had been forwarded to the committee from Marseille, listing, under our name, a bicycle: "One bicycle, red; tires in a state of deterioration." Did we wish to recover this property? We said no.

Peter, at the time, was a senior in medical school, in Chicago.

M. Zuckerberg's Heart

I ARRIVED in America, a refugee doctor, in late summer of
1941, and in November I began to study English in prep-
aration for a test by the New York State Board of Medical Examiners. Classes, which were arranged by the Reset-
tlement Committee for Foreign Physicians, were held in an
old auditorium on Lexington Avenue near Ninety-first
Street. I lived with my wife and son in the mid-Seventies
on the West Side. When I had a nickel, I commuted by
crosstown bus; otherwise, I walked across Central Park.
Even when the weather grew wintry, these walks had a
certain charm for me, for they reminded me of my house
calls to the villages surrounding Mattersburg, the town in
Austria where I had practiced. In those days, instead of
using my car, I often chose to trudge across the empty
white cornfields in the stinging air.

One snowy day early in December, I was returning from class along Broadway, my head down against the wind, when I bumped into someone coming from the opposite direction. The English-study notebook I was carrying fell to the sidewalk. I retrieved it and straightened up, and I found myself looking into a familiar face—birdlike, with a wingspread of giant ears. "M. Zuckerberg!" I said.

M. Zuckerberg (as I will call my friend) embraced me, kissing me on both cheeks. "*Mais Docteur, c'est pas possible!*" he shouted. "How wonderful to see you alive!" His French still retained a faint East European accent.

We went to the Tip Toe Inn, at the corner of Eighty-sixth Street and Broadway, and sat at a table by a window.

"I am healthy, Doctor," M. Zuckerberg announced at once. "You wouldn't believe it, but, *parole d'honneur*, I don't need a doctor anymore. But tell me, how are Maria and Peter? When did you get here?"

"We're all fine," I said. "We arrived in August."

"From Bordeaux?"

"No, Marseille, then Morocco—"

"Morocco! Then you didn't fall into the hands of those bastards who were taking refugees to Portugal. Do you know what the captain of a Spanish freighter wanted? Ten thousand dollars! What could I do? The Nazis were at the outskirts of Bordeaux. I gave him almost all I had, and my wife gave him her necklace, which was worth at least five thousand. I had just about enough left for two tickets on an American boat—tourist class—and we came to New York. It was August a year ago." He grinned. "Do you know what I'm doing? I run an elevator on Riverside Drive. My wife works in a doll factory!"

Back in Neuilly-sur-Seine, in the suburbs of Paris, M. Zuckerberg had owned a mammoth sawmill. I met him in Paris, where we had fled after the Anschluss, through an old friend of mine, Hans Klein, who had come to Paris four years earlier. Klein was a psychoanalyst, one of the closest to Freud, and in Paris he had joined the psychoanalytical society, which didn't require one to have a license to practice. I was a general practitioner, and, like hundreds of other refugee physicians, was left alienated from my profession by the need of an unattainable piece of paper. So when I ran into Klein one day in April, 1938, I was eager to hear about his good luck. A Gauloise Bleue hung from his lips, and he had developed a taste for Pernod; otherwise, he was Klein from the Praterstrasse in Vienna. We sat in the Café Weber in the Rue Royale and talked at length about possibilities for getting me established; there seemed no way of circumventing the license problem.

Suddenly Klein slapped his forehead and exclaimed, "Why, for God's sake, didn't I think of Zuckerberg? He is just the case for you. What he wants is a personal physician. He was my patient when I first came to Paris, but after a while I got so busy with my practice I had to give the old man up. He's a businessman, tremendously successful, and rich! Anyhow, he needs a good, down-to-earth general practitioner. Are you interested? Wait here." He ran to a telephone booth, talked for some time, and then came back with a broad smile on his face. "You always were lucky in a critical moment," he said. "Really, it's fantastic that we ran into each other. It's settled. I convinced him you are the right man. Tomorrow, at eight in the morning, he expects you at his factory." He wrote down the address on the margin of a *Paris-Midi*. "Give me a ring afterward," he said.

Next morning at six, I set out for Neuilly. It was a

complicated trip; after the last Métro stop, I had to change buses three times to get to the address Klein had given me: a giant square filled with timber. The air resounded with the noise of wood saws, and a fine snow of sawdust fell upon me. In the office, a young, very pretty girl was manicuring her nails and humming a popular song that went *"J'attendrai, le jour et la nuit j'attendrai toujours."* She refused to believe that M. Zuckerberg was waiting for me. "Every salesman says the same."

"But I am a doctor," I said.

"Mon Dieu!" she exclaimed, and rushed to a loudspeaker.

Hardly a second later, a man stormed through the door. "Where is the doctor?" he shouted. He was clad like a lumberjack, in torn overalls—a man of about sixty, six feet two and broad-shouldered. "I am M. Zuckerberg," he announced. "Follow me!"

We entered his office. He closed the door and brusquely stripped to the waist. I took my stethoscope from one pocket and blood-pressure apparatus from another. I examined him thoroughly while he rested on a couch. I noticed that he had a large scar above his right eyebrow. After I had finished, I said, "You are all right."

"Listen, once again," he said. "At the insertion of the left fourth rib on the sternum there is a murmur."

I listened again. "No murmur," I said.

"Dr. *Klein* always found the murmur."

"I don't hear it."

"Didn't he tell you that I have heart disease?"

"No."

M. Zuckerberg pulled up his overalls. "At 8 P.M. I expect you at my home," he said. "With your suitcase."

"I don't understand," I said.

"You're my personal physician, aren't you? Didn't Klein tell you anything? I need to have a doctor at hand.

You will sleep in the room next to mine. Around eleven at night, I have palpitations and dyspnea. And even during the day it happens occasionally. There's a comfortable room here at the mill for you to use during the day. Any books you want you just have to ask for. You'll have them next day. Your salary will be three thousand a month and full maintenance. Agreed?"

"No," I said, without hesitation.

He looked at me from curious little eyes; his lower lip reached upward, touching his nose. "All right," he said. "I can get refugee doctors—as many as I want."

"That's fine with me," I said.

"Wait a minute," he said. "I'll give you five hundred more."

"But you don't understand," I said. "I'm married and have a small child."

M. Zuckerberg paced up and down. "O.K. I'll give you two afternoons off."

"Let me think it over."

"At 8 P.M. sharp! *Au revoir.*"

When I got back to the small hotel where we lived, I telephoned Klein. "It's absolute slavery," I said. "What is this man?"

"A perfect regression into *Kindheitsideen*—the primitive fear of a three-year-old child. It's nothing. Anyway, it's a temporary job. Don't be an idiot."

I discussed everything with my wife, Maria. We had no choice. At eight in the evening, I rang the bell at a door on the Avenue de la Grande-Armée. A servant in livery opened the door and led me to my room, which was furnished in Empire style. I had hardly had time to unpack my clothing when the same servant entered, bowed, and announced that dinner was served.

Around the table, the family was assembled—Mme. Zuckerberg, in a blue evening gown with a deep décolletage, M. Zuckerberg and his son, an overfed teen-ager, in tuxedos. Mme. Zuckerberg had a fine oval face and warm brown eyes; compared to her husband, she looked tiny. But during the meal she led the conversation, speaking a fast Parisian French. The impending visit of the British royal couple was the talk of Paris, and Mme. Zuckerberg thought it would be a deterrent to any ambitions Hitler might have for conquering Europe. *"N'est-ce pas?"* She turned to me. *"Il est fou!"*

The meal was superb. At the beginning, I felt self-conscious in my business suit, which was not even freshly pressed, but soon I took part in the conversation. I agreed with Mme. Zuckerberg about the Führer's mental status but thought that more should be done to check his ambitions. Mme. Zuckerberg assented. Her husband was mostly silent, uttering only a few "Hmm"s.

After dinner, I went up to my room, lay down on a couch, and read a book called "La Rue du Chat-qui-Pêche," which dealt with the problems of refugees in Paris. I heard M. Zuckerberg pacing up and down in his room. Then I fell asleep. I awoke to find M. Zuckerberg standing before me in his nightshirt; he was panting heavily and calling my name. He tottered back to his room and lay down on his bed. I placed my stethoscope on his chest. His heartbeat was regular, his chest clear and free of rales.

"You are all right," I said. I must have sounded slightly annoyed.

M. Zuckerberg sat up. "Repeat it," he said.

"You're all right. Fine, fine fine!"

"You sound convincing," he said, and lay back. A few minutes later, he was snoring peacefully.

A servant woke me at six. After I finished my toilet, I found M. Zuckerberg sitting at a breakfast table that had been set up on the terrace outside his bedroom. It was a wonderfully clear spring morning, and there was an uninterrupted view to the Place de la Concorde at the end of the Champs-Élysées. M. Zuckerberg looked rested and had rosy cheeks; his appetite was splendid. After breakfast, we went downstairs, where a large black Citroën was waiting, a uniformed chauffeur standing at attention by the open door. He bowed as we entered the car.

In Neuilly, M. Zuckerberg changed into his overalls, and I was taken to my daytime quarters—a comfortable room stacked with books. Through a window, I watched M. Zuckerberg lift heavy pieces of lumber and gesture and shout at his workers. At intervals, he would stagger into my room, panting, and ask for an examination.

We returned to the Avenue de la Grande-Armée, had dinner, and retired to our rooms.

At eleven that night, M. Zuckerberg had his regular attack. And so it went, day after day. His energy remained undiminished, but soon I was exhausted. One night after his attack, I said to him, "M. Zuckerberg, won't you tell me a bit about these fears of yours? After all—"

His tousled black eyebrows lifted. "I hired you as a G.P., didn't I?"

"Yes, but you are healthy. There must be psychological reasons for your complaints."

"For *those*, I have an analyst," he said in a curt voice. "Three times a week—five hundred francs a session. *He* investigates my Oedipus complex. Now let me sleep. Tomorrow I have a busy day."

In spite of this exchange, little by little something like a human relationship developed between us. One week, he offered me a third afternoon off. Mme. Zuckerberg would invite me for walks in their beautiful park, explaining to me how hard it was to cultivate exotic flowers in the uneven Paris climate. She was an educated woman, well read. She loved baroque music. Often we would sit in the park, talking. She would tell me what a kind, fine man her husband was—a tender, understanding being, although a self-made man. "But what a life," she said one time, weeping, "with a doctor as his sleeping companion!" I could have wept with her.

In the middle of the summer, I accompanied M. Zuckerberg on a business trip to Rumania, where he bought forests in the mountains of Transylvania. From Bucharest we travelled to Rome, where M. Zuckerberg negotiated with the Italian government to plant trees in the dried Pontine Marshes. From Rome we took the train north, along the Italian Riviera to the Côte d'Azur, to rest. As we travelled through San Remo, Ospedaletti, Bordighera, the scent of blooming roses everywhere filled our compartment. The change of scene had done nothing for my patient's complaint. He slept in the lower berth, and at his familiar summons I would crawl down the ladder with my stethoscope and blood-pressure apparatus. Afterward, I would listen to M. Zuckerberg's sonorous snoring until the dawn filtered through the fringes of the drawn curtains.

It was in Marseille, after returning from the diner one evening, that M. Zuckerberg, in a reflective mood, finally spoke of his past. "You're a fine, smart man," he said. "And I'm a dope. I make millions, and I even have the Officer's Cross of the Legion of Honor. But what the hell do I get out of my fortune! Nothing. Doctors, doctors, and again doctors. What a pity." He sank back on the plush seat of the compartment. Taking long pauses, he told me his story.

He was born and raised in Kishinev, a Russian town inhabited by many Jews, near the Rumanian border. He was the youngest of eight children, all boys. All would eventually have to serve in the Czar's Army, a terrible ordeal for Jewish boys. There was no legal way of getting a passport for a boy so that he could escape to a foreign country, and the Zuckerbergs decided on a desperate measure to save one son at least. They would raise the youngest, Moishe, as a girl. In the town's registry, he was entered as "Judith." He wore girl's clothes. The secret was kept among fellow-Jews. Years passed. Around the turn of the century, there was a pogrom in Kishinev that in cruelty surpassed any of the routine pogroms in the realm of the Czar. Several of the Zuckerberg boys and their father were killed, and Moishe-Judith's forehead was struck by a Cossack's sabre. It was after this that the mother applied for passports for herself and her daughter—quite a problem, for the girl had grown into a giant. Somehow, they obtained them and made their way to Paris. There, for the first time in his life, Moishe (now called Marcel) wore men's clothing. He was twenty-one years old.

"I have told my story a hundred times to psychiatrists," M. Zuckerberg continued, "but they say that my psychological trauma developed long before my forced 'transvestism,' as they call it. Who knows? Doctor, please be honest —is my heart really healthy?"

"It is, M. Zuckerberg," I said. "Believe me!"

In the fall of 1938, I received a commission as a physician on the Ivory Coast, and I left M. Zuckerberg in the care of another refugee G.P. A year later, I returned to Paris and again became his physician—or, rather, his consultant, for he kept his other G.P. as a routine watchdog. The money I received for my services became the backbone of our meagre income. In June, 1940, before the Germans entered Paris, I once more said goodbye to M. Zuckerberg. On this occasion, he said, "*Au revoir, Docteur.* I hope we shall meet again in this life."

———

THE waitresses of the Tip Toe Inn began to set the tables for dinner. M. Zuckerberg ordered another cup of coffee. "The last one," he promised. We had talked for nearly an hour, mostly about our hasty exits from Europe.

"*Alors, cher Docteur,*" M. Zuckerberg said in summation. "*C'est la vie.* My son is a prisoner of war in Germany. He sends us letters through the Red Cross. I know the Boches don't feed their prisoners too well. His mother always cautioned him not to eat so much. Poor Étienne." He looked reflective for a moment. "Tell me—you haven't said what you do besides study English. Are you earning a living?"

"You wouldn't believe it," I said, "but I'm precisely in the state I was in when I first met you—penniless and waiting for a damned license!"

"Ah," said M. Zuckerberg. "*Je regrette beaucoup que je ne peux pas vous aider.*" A deeply troubled look crossed his face, and then he laughed. "But well, what's the use of thinking what it would be like if I still needed my doctors!"

"By the way," I said, "how did it stop—the palpitations you complained about."

Zuckerberg's eyes became brighter, and he smiled. "It was in Lisbon. Finally, we got there from Bordeaux. Safety! The only thing we could afford was one of those small hotels near the port—no bathroom, no decent plumbing, and one bedroom for the first time in our married lives! We were very tired after our trip and went to bed early. I lay wide awake, thinking what would happen two hours from then, and what it would be like later, here in New York, without money, and no house doctor, no psychiatrist, no consultant. I felt helpless, abandoned. I needed someone to talk to. I spoke to Alice. No answer. I had never known what a sound sleeper Alice was. She began to snore while I was talking to her. I looked at my watch; it was nine. And then I must have fallen asleep, too.

Suddenly I felt that familiar tight feeling in my throat." He clutched his throat and simulated a look of fright. "I opened my eyes. Broad daylight! I shook Alice and said, 'Can you imagine, I slept through the entire night!' She opened one eye, looked at me in disbelief, and went back to sleep. The following night, no palpitations; the next night, no palpitations; and since then, *none!* I've often thought what brought that change about. Didn't my heart become stronger because I needed it more? What do you think, Doctor?" He picked up the check. He did not look at me. "Just the same, Doctor," he said, in a wistful voice, "would you mind listening to my heart—occasionally?"

I said I would be glad to.

We stood. M. Zuckerberg slapped the table. "It's the only good thing that son of a bitch Hitler did for me," he said.

Our Maximilian

I N the summer of 1963, I left my medical practice in New York and returned to Austria with my wife for two weeks of rest in the mountains near Salzburg and a longer stay in Vienna, where I revisited familiar places of my medical-student days. It was my first trip back since 1950. The day before our holiday ended, we set out on a journey to my home province—Burgenland, on the Hungarian border —a drive of about two hours from the center of Vienna, through Eisenstadt, where Haydn lived and is buried; through Raiding, the birthplace of Franz Liszt; and on through towns and hamlets filled with the small, chalk-white houses of peasants. Endless fields of corn and wheat had just been harvested. Bright-red poppies covered the meadows.

Our destination was the town of Lackenbach, where

my mother's ancestors had lived for five hundred years. My grandmother is buried there. When I was twelve years old, I had gone to her grave with my mother—my father was a soldier and away fighting in the First World War. My grandmother had died the year before. This, I suddenly realized, was the fiftieth anniversary of her death, and I decided to visit her grave.

I remembered where the cemetery was—along a narrow path on a hill behind the synagogue on Judengasse— but everything had changed. On Judengasse, the Jewish names above the haberdasheries were gone; the squat, sombre synagogue had been erased; and the narrow path on the hill behind had become a street. We could not see the cemetery. My wife and I walked back and forth, but we could not locate it, and finally I asked a mustachioed old man who was basking in the sun where the *Judenfriedhof* was. He pointed. A house had been built on the small square in front of the cemetery entrance, completely obscuring it. The old man led us across a vegetable garden and then across a yard where chickens were pecking corn. At last, we stood in front of a rusted gate. The old man turned the key for us.

I still search for a word to describe the loneliness of that derelict meadow. Hundreds of tombstones had been tossed to the ground and lay half hidden among thick grass. Did anyone care for the cemetery, I asked the old man. No one, he said. Not one of the four hundred Jews who had lived in the town remained. Occasionally, said the old man, somebody would come from a faraway place and stand at the cemetery entrance, saying prayers.

I went to the corner where my grandmother's grave was, in the midst of the oldest graves. I remembered a shining black tombstone engraved with tiny Hebrew characters and, at the bottom, the family name in gold letters.

This corner, too, was littered with fallen, half-buried tombstones. The old man helped me turn some of them over. On one I saw fading gold and thought I had found my grandmother's grave, but the letters spelled an unfamiliar name. I continued to pick my way around the cemetery, and once I found myself speaking aloud, asking my grandmother where she was.

My wife said, "Please, let's go. She knows you were here."

We drove back to Vienna in silence. During the trip, I was haunted by the image of my grandmother, an old woman in her bonnet and shawl, leaning heavily on a cane. She lived with us when I was a child, in an apartment one reached by entering a hall, which always smelled faintly of mildew, and then climbing a winding staircase. I recalled how I used to go to her room. Inevitably, I recalled Maximilian.

———————◄————

Our handsome Archduke Maximilian had been killed— shot in far-off Mexico—thirty-five years before I was born, but he was made a living creature when my grandmother described him. There he was, just as she had seen him in her youth, and she would point to the fading, colored print that hung on the wall of her bedroom. It did not do him justice, of course. "*Ach*, Richard," she used to say, "you should have seen the man himself!"

How often I stared up at the young man on his huge white horse. I studied the jaunty shako with its sprouting green feathers, the blue coat on fire with gleaming medals. In the print, the friendly face looked down on a dozen generals seated on smaller horses. Opposite the grand Maximilian stood a man in morning coat, with a top hat in his hand. Nearby were musicians with solemn faces, trumpets at their lips. There were clergy in black robes. And, everywhere, children—stiff-necked boys with mouths open, and curly-haired girls in white dresses.

I loved to be in Grandmother's room, filled with the scent of lavender from the mysterious chest where she kept her daguerreotypes and the beloved *Tagebuch* in which she made entries every night. I remember visiting her one winter day. There was new snow and a high wind, and after school I had played in the streets until my hands and feet were numb. Up in her room, I sat next to the tiny iron stove in the corner, warm, listening as she told her story:

"Well, our Army had *Kaisermanöver* in the hills near Lackenbach. We had heard that the Emperor's brother, Archduke Maximilian, would come to command one of the opposing squadrons in the maneuvers. Every day there was much excitement, with soldiers arriving, filling the inns, and things happened that a little boy should not be told. It was August. *Very* hot. Finally, the day came when they said he would be here. Some said he would only pass through; others said no, he would stay awhile. In either case, we wanted to pay our respects. Early in the morning, we met at school and marched to the crossroad outside town, to stand along the road to greet him. Our teachers went with us. The whole town was there, including the mayor, who kept taking off his hat to wipe his bald head. There was the priest, and the choirboys, and the town band, which had been playing marches since five o'clock. The mayor made a speech. He told us exactly what we must do. When the procession came along, the bugler would sound the *Generalmarsch*, then the band would play the *Kaiserlied*, and we were all to sing—first very quietly and then very loud. The church bells would toll, too. If the coach of the Archduke should go slowly and the *Kaiserlied* should end before he had quite passed, we would have to start again."

At that point, Grandmother interrupted herself to hum a few bars of the *Kaiserlied*. She held her hand out, with one long, quivering finger pointed directly at me, as though she feared I might break the spell. "It became eleven o'clock," she continued. "Then twelve, then one, and our great guest had not arrived. The teachers could not keep us quiet, and we were led back to school. The musicians were weary, and they headed for the taverns, and the mayor went home. Then, about two hours later, we heard from far away the sound of trumpets. Along came the mayor in his shirt-sleeves, and the two town drummers, running through the streets, sounding the warning. Running along behind was the mayor's wife, carrying his coat. By the time we got to the crossroad, there was the head of the procession—thirty soldiers on beautiful black horses. How fine they were! Behind them was a huge, gilded carriage, and, to our surprise, it stopped. We began to sing. You have never heard singing so loud. *'Gott erhalte, Gott beschütze, unsern Kaiser, unser Land!'* The Archduke stepped out of the carriage in his beautiful blue uniform with its crosses and stars, and we sang even louder. *'Gott erhalte, Gott beschütze'*— But then the Archduke raised his hand. 'Quiet!' he shouted. Naturally, everyone was quiet."

Just then the door of Grandmother's room opened, letting in light from the kitchen. My mother was standing there, and back of her I could see Mariska, our maid, stirring the fire with the poker. "What's going on here?" Mother asked.

"A story," I said. "Grandmother is telling me a story."

"Did you finish your homework?"

"Please," I said, "let her finish the story."

"Mama!" Mother said sharply, turning to Grand-mother.

"He is learning history," said Grandmother.

"History? You call it history, the tales you tell the boy?"

"Tales?" Grandmother leaned forward. "You would call the story about the unhappy Maximilian a tale?"

There was no more of the story that evening. Grandmother followed us out to the kitchen and lighted the kerosene lamp for me, and I began the incomprehensible nightly batch of arithmetic problems.

I was not to hear the rest of the Maximilian story for a while. When I took Grandmother for our walks, she deftly changed the subject whenever I asked her to tell me more. Had my mother put an end to it forever, I wondered, and if so why? One evening, unexpectedly, the story was resumed. We were sitting in the kitchen. When I think of our kitchen, I think of goose feathers. It isn't possible, but it seems to me that geese were plucked there every night in the wintertime. The small white pile on the table would grow to a hill, then a mountain, as my grandmother, mother, and, after her dishwashing, Mariska plucked and gossiped. I sat nearby, ostensibly doing my homework but listening to every word.

When I heard Grandmother begin the Maximilian story, I tried to appear especially diligent with my lessons. Before long, we were at the point where the Archduke had raised his hand and called out, "Quiet!"

"Naturally," Grandmother said, "everyone was quiet. '*I will a Glas Wasser habn; i bin durschti*,' said the Archduke. He spoke in the old dialect. Well, we were all thirsty, it was so hot. But there was no water around, and the village was ten minutes from the crossroad. The mayor was very embarrassed and would have gone back himself for some water, but before he could think, the Archduke had got back into his carriage and ordered it to start moving. 'Such a pigsty,' I heard the coachman say as he lifted his whip.

The poor mayor sat down on the grass. 'I, too, need a glass of water,' he said."

Mariska laughed, and I saw Grandmother give her a reproachful glance. But she went on with her story. We heard of Franz Josef, the young Kaiser, and of his ambitious mother, the Archduchess Sophie, who was determined that her second son—Maximilian—should become an emperor. Grandmother grew excited as she spoke of the ruthless Napoleon III of France, who had his *"blutbefleckte Hände"* in the intrigue. She told of the beautiful Charlotte, now wedded to the glorious Maximilian, and of a ball in Vienna, in the glittering Hofburg. It was held to honor Maximilian and Charlotte, who were soon to become the rulers of Mexico. Johann Strauss the younger and his orchestra played quadrilles and waltzes, as guests from all over the monarchy danced the night through. It was a superb, fitting farewell to the hero who was on his way to oppose the "wicked, wicked murderers." After the festivities in Vienna, there were still more in Paris, where Napoleon and Eugénie entertained the young couple handsomely.

"But that Napoleon was up to no good," said Grandmother with disgust. "Imagine! He called Maximilian 'brother,' and praised him, and all the while he knew what was coming. Right after Maximilian arrived in Mexico, he realized the people were all against him. His army had no equipment, and was not large enough. He sent messages to Napoleon, asking for help, but of course no help came. He sent his wife, Charlotte, but Napoleon was too busy even to see her. All the while, that awful Juarez was leading his men closer and closer, until finally they encircled the poor little army of Maximilian. There was no hope, and Maximilian was taken prisoner." Sadly, Grandmother told how the Emperor had been humiliated, and how he had taken off his sabre and put it on the table before Juarez.

At that point, I abandoned my lessons. "He should have thrown it in Juarez' face," I said. "The dirty bastard!" "Don't speak like that!" my mother said. She turned to Grandmother. "Mama, *please*. You are upsetting the boy!" "*Bitte*," said Grandmother. Then she spoke to me. "Your mother is right, Richard. You shouldn't use such expressions. At any rate, our poor Maximilian was executed, in a place called Querétaro. But before they shot him he embraced his two remaining faithful generals, who were also to die with him. 'I thank you,' he said. 'I thank you from the bottom of my heart. A wicked enemy has vanquished us, and we must die. I think of my homeland, my wife, my glorious brother . . .'" Grandmother's voice broke off, and she scooped a pile of feathers into a sack. "And now, Richard, you must go to bed."

THIRTY years later, Grandmother, of course, was dead. Mother and Father had long since left Lackenbach for Vienna. Mother was a fragile, bent old lady, enduring severe diabetes and a constantly threatening heart condition. She did not sit and brood about her ailments but walked with my father every day in the park of the Lichtenstein palace, opposite the old building where they lived. Father was retired from public office; he had held the title of *Regierungsrat*—chief administrator of the Burgenland health-and-welfare program.

It was the Vienna of the Anschluss. The old Austrian empire of Franz Josef and Maximilian was gone, and now the Austrian republic that succeeded it had been extinguished in the demoniac months of March and April, 1938. Mother couldn't believe it. She looked about her at the conservative, upper-middle-class neighborhood and still

found serenity. Noise of marching boots had not yet penetrated the Lichtensteinstrasse. "What could possibly happen to us old people?" she would ask when I spoke of the
seriousness of the new developments. "Your father has his
pension. Forty years of service, after all!"

Meanwhile, my younger brother, Pali, was arrested;
my older brother, Arpad, a surgeon in the General Hospital, was forcibly removed from his job and badly beaten;
and finally I, too, was arrested, in Mattersburg, where I
was the town doctor. After a month, I was released, and
with my wife and young son moved in with my parents
and set about getting a visa to any country in the world
that was willing to receive us and our parents. In warm,
balmy days and through entire nights, I would wait in
front of embassies. It seemed hopeless. I would come home
weary, disappointed.

Mother would try to be comforting. *"Geduld, geduld* [Pa-
tience, patience]," she would say. "Soup is never eaten as
hot as it is prepared. These crazy ones will also cool down.
Austrians are never violent."

But one day the Nazis came to the little apartment on
the Lichtensteinstrasse. I returned home just in time to see
my father being put into a police van. His long, passive
face was pale, but composed as always, in spite of his being
pushed by two S.A. youngsters, who were yelling at him,
"Come on! Can't you walk?" Mother stood in the doorway,
looking very small, shaking her head. Another pair of S.A.
men were carrying our silver down in a basket. She stepped
aside to let them pass, and stared, in a trancelike state, at
the heaping basket.

A few days later, Father was back. He brought with
him a copy of a document he had signed. He had "volunteered" to relinquish all claims to his pension. Slowly, the
realization came over Mother that times had indeed
changed.

I redoubled my efforts. I wrote letters to people all over the world—to friends, to unknown persons whose names I dug up from telephone directories, to anyone who might offer us some chance of escape. I had information that I was soon to be arrested again, so I began sleeping at night in the homes of friends. Replies to my letters, when I got any, arrived *poste restante*.

On the tenth of April, I went to the post office to collect my mail. There was only one letter, and I could envisage its contents: one more dreary message—no assistance. But this one was different. After reading it, I ran all the way home. "Mama!" I cried. "It's come at last. We have a visa!"

She had a pot of water in her hand, and stood with her back to me. She twisted her head around. "A visa? A visa. Good. And to where, Richard? To what country?"

"To Mexico," I said.

"Mexico?"

"Yes, Mama. Mexico."

She turned to face me. "No. No, I would not *think* of it," she said. "To a country where they murdered our Maximilian I do not go."

She would not consent to leave Austria until several months later, when there were rumors that the Gestapo was intending to arrest Father again. At that time, my wife, my little son, and I were already in Paris, and I had succeeded in obtaining French visas for my parents. After the defeat of France, they escaped to the United States. Mother died in 1944. She is buried in a cemetery on Long Island.

Matura

I FLED from my home town, Sopron, in Hungary, when I was eighteen. During the First World War, I had been the leader of a student pacifist movement at the *Gymnasium*, and I had also taken part in the two revolutions that followed the war. When Admiral Horthy successfully staged his counter-revolution, I was expelled from school by the new Fascist regime, imprisoned, and forbidden to attend any other *Gymnasium* in Hungary. As soon as I was released from prison, I escaped to Austria. My situation as an émigré was miserable, but what I regretted most was that I had been forced to leave school just before my final examinations and therefore did not receive the much coveted *Matura*, the Certificate of Maturity, which, under solemn circumstances, was presented to graduates from the *Gymnasium*. Although in Vienna I made up for my interrupted studies and entered medical school, I could not seem to rid myself of the disappointment. Even decades later, a nightmarish dream repeated itself: I stood before my class in Sopron, unable to recite my lessons. I had forgotten math, biology, physics, history—all my subjects. I would never get the *Matura*, never.

As time passed, ties with my home town slackened to an occasional greeting card from distant relatives (my parents and brothers left Hungary soon after me) and a few schoolmates, and finally ceased. Before the Second World War, I emigrated to France, and eventually to America, so I was separated geographically, too. It seemed unlikely that I would ever again hear any news from Sopron. But at the end of 1944 Sopron made the headlines. The war communiqués announced that this westernmost city of Hungary had been stubbornly defended by the Nazis and their Hungarian allies against the onstorming Red Army. The strategic location of Sopron, half enclosed by mountains, had made its defense easier, but finally the city fell. What Turks and Tartars in past history could not achieve the Russians did. Although, of course, I was glad to see the Nazis defeated, I was somehow sorry. I could imagine how badly the town had been damaged—my school, the little baroque house where I was born, destroyed.

For another two decades, I heard nothing further. Then in the spring of 1965 an envelope postmarked Sopron arrived at my office in New York, where I had been practicing medicine for a good many years. The envelope contained a printed invitation to the forty-fifth reunion of the class of 1920 on the last Saturday in June—the traditional day for graduations. In Hungary, *Gymnasium* reunions take place with regularity as long as any alumni are still alive. A note from the principal of the school, a Mr. Laky, accompanied the invitation. He hoped that I would be able to attend. "The teaching staff, the pupils, and last but not least your former schoolmates will be happy to greet you, who have achieved fame in the outside world," he wrote. My whereabouts had been discovered through the publication of one of my stories in a Viennese magazine.

I was greatly touched by the invitation. Homesickness, intense when I first left Sopron, had passed away with the years, but I still had a desire to see the places of my youth. At the end of the Second World War, I longed to revisit my home town. But then had come the terrible reports that the Jews of Sopron had been deported to extermination camps, and that the Hungarians had behaved no better— even worse—than the Germans. I thought at the time I could never go back into that world where all those close to me had been murdered. As I reread the invitation, I found that my feelings had altered. A new generation had arisen, I told myself—a generation free of guilt. Wouldn't it now be possible to see everything with my own eyes, without anguish?

My wife opposed the trip, and so did everyone I spoke to. At best, they said, it would be visiting graves. After deliberation, I answered the principal with a gently worded letter, avoiding anything that might offend the sponsors of the reunion—professional obligations made it impossible to leave my office in June; I had already planned a vacation to Europe for the month of August. And I added that I was not a bona-fide member of the class of '20—I had not achieved the *Matura*.

Two weeks later, I received a second letter from the principal. The anniversary celebrations had been postponed to the last Saturday in August, he wrote, and as to my argument about not being a member of the class of 1920, it had no validity. Hadn't I been expelled by the Fascists? Was I willing to accept their verdict? Of course not. I would be greeted with open arms.

This time, I said to my wife, I could not refuse—anyway, during the last week in August we would be only a few miles away, in Vienna. My wife remained adamant, and so we compromised; while I made my overnight trip to Sopron she would remain in Vienna.

—————

At eight o'clock on a sunny August morning, I left Vienna to travel the eighty kilometres to Sopron. The ceremonies had been scheduled for noon, and I remembered that the trip took three hours or a bit longer. The Reichstrasse led through numerous towns and villages. One slow-moving cart—to be expected at harvest-time—could bring traffic to a standstill. And thirty kilometres from the Austro-Hungarian border the road to Sopron branched off the main route; it was a dirt road, and that would be slow.

But I found that things had changed. A modern Autobahn now bypassed the populated places, and the dirt road had been paved. After only an hour and twenty minutes, I arrived at the Austrian frontier. The customs official, a typical *gemütlich* civil servant, barely glanced at my passport and wished me a *gute Reise*. I continued on the narrow strip of no man's land to a level-crossing gate painted with the red, white, and green colors of Hungary. The gate rose high, and I drove into a wide square surrounded by barbed wire. The Hungarian flag flew from the eaves of the customs house—the old flag, except that the crown of St. Stephen had yielded to a red star.

A soldier wearing tight breeches and high boots—a Russian-style uniform—approached my car and in broken German asked for my passport. The Volkswagen I had rented in Vienna naturally bore Austrian license plates. Much to his surprise, I answered in Hungarian and at the same time presented him with my American passport.

"How come?" he asked, pointing suspiciously at my passport. I explained that I had been born in Hungary and had left many years before but had never forgotten my mother tongue. "That's another matter," he said, obviously pleased, and he smiled as he shifted his carbine higher on his shoulder. He was a handsome, very young man, with closely set black eyes. While he took my passport to the customs building, I gazed ahead to the mountains that encircled Sopron, only two kilometres away. The soldier returned with my passport and wished me a good journey. I waved goodbye to him, my first countryman.

A few minutes later, I turned a sharp curve, and there was the panorama of Sopron trickling down the hills to its compact center in the valley.

In a long and enthusiastic response to my acceptance of his invitation, Laky wrote that he had made a reservation for me at the Red Star Hotel, on the main boulevard. I did not recall a hotel of that name and assumed it was one that had not existed in my time. When I arrived, I was amazed to find that it was the good old Hotel to the Hungarian King, a bit shabbier, and scarred with bullets. Over the flag on a rusty signboard was the image of the King, with crown and sceptre; he alone seemed to have survived the change of his realm into a Communist state.

I parked my car right at the hotel entrance. There were no other cars in sight. (I learned there were only two taxis of prewar model and one newer, official car in town.) As I took my suitcase from the luggage compartment, a man in a black jacket with gold buttons rushed out to meet me. "Are you Berczeller *doktor úr?*" he said. (In Hungarian, titles and other forms of address are put after a name.) I nodded yes and he bowed slightly. "I am Boross *elvtárs* [comrade]," he said, adding that I was expected later. He was the hotel clerk and, he said smilingly, Jack-of-all-trades. He took my suitcase and opened the door with a grand gesture. He was a man about fifty, with a round gypsy face and a trimmed mustache.

Before the war, all hotels, even at the remotest corners of the Austro-Hungarian Empire, had emulated the big hotels in Vienna: giant lobbies with columns, thick carpets, luxurious sofas along the walls, deep chairs upholstered in red, crystal chandeliers. When I was a boy, I had thought that the Hotel to the Hungarian King was the only one of its kind and was immensely proud of it. Now the carpeting had disappeared, the chairs and sofas were worn, and the crystal had been replaced by shaded bulbs. Boross *elvtárs* followed my glance at the ceiling. "Direct hit, with your kind permission," he said with an expression of regret. Pictures of Schönbrunn and of the Hofburg still hung on the walls, but the portrait of Franz Josef had been displaced by one of Lenin.

Several guests sitting in the lobby looked up from their newspapers when I entered. I studied the gentlemen with gray hair or bald heads, wondering if one or another could be a former schoolmate. None of them appeared to recognize me, and in a moment they returned to their reading. Boross urged me to follow him. The room on the second floor into which he led me was furnished with yellow embroidered draperies, a faded Oriental carpet, and a large bed piled high with quilts and covered with a yellow velvet spread. Boross *elvtárs* was biting his mustache, apparently waiting for my response to all that opulence. In a capitalist country I knew how to express my gratitude, but weren't tips forbidden in the Communist world? Still, I took a twenty-forint bill (eighty cents in American currency) from my pocket and held it out on my palm. Those gypsy eyes widened, and with an elegant gesture Boross *elvtárs* lifted the bill into an upper pocket of his vest. Bowing, he left.

I opened the window and looked out over the gabled, medieval roofs. The bluish silhouettes of mountains—the spurs of the Alps, already partly covered by snow—looked deceptively near. The scent of the approaching autumn, which starts early in that part of the world, filled the clear air. From the moment my car had rumbled on Sopron's old cobblestones, forty-five years of absence had vanished. Now I felt I could not wait to see the town. I left my suitcase unpacked and walked down to the lobby. I had two and a half hours before the reunion.

The boulevard was now called Lenin körút. What had been a solid row of one- and two-story buildings was interrupted here and there by dark holes—ruins still, twenty years after the war. I looked in vain for the Café Hungaria, our hideout, where, in the back room, we boys had smoked forbidden cigarettes and played billiards—a deadly sin for pupils of the *Gymnasium*. Once, we were so deeply involved in our play we didn't notice Mr. Harsányi, our math teacher—the spy who investigated the illegal activities of the student body—standing at the door. I was no good in math but was excellent at billiards. Mr. Harsányi directed what I considered his cruel eyes at me while I was holding the cue. To my amazement, he challenged me to a game. I beat him three times in a row, although my hands were trembling. "*Ejnye, ejnye* [Look, look]," he cried, shaking his head. "I wonder how such a stupid boy can be so good at billiards." Nevertheless, from then on my marks in math improved. There was another dark hole where the building with the candy store had been—where we would stand about for long stretches of time, unable to decide which of the multicolored sweets we would choose. The lending library, with its Nick Carters, Sherlock Holmeses, Buffalo Bills, had given way to a dark hole, and so had the house where I had taken dancing lessons.

Not every landmark was gone. The *elökapu*, the entrance door to the medieval inner city, and the high, Gothic city tower, although riddled with bullet and grenade holes, both stood in place, and the baroque column commemorating a plague in the seventeenth century—a tall monument, striving toward heaven, an ideal target—also stood unharmed. But a block of houses only a stone's throw away had vanished, and in its place a triangular park had been laid out with grass and acacia trees. An uncle of mine, a physician, had lived, with his family, in one of those houses. He died of natural causes before the Second World War, but his widow and little daughter had perished in an extermination camp. Beyond the little park, I walked winding streets so narrow that one could touch the buildings on either side, and then I came to the house where I was born and spent my early years. Although the walls were pocked, the fine baroque ornaments framing the windows had not been touched. But the tall lime trees in the courtyard (Grandmother used to tell how a former owner, a bishop, planted them two hundred years before) had been hacked out, and there was now an unhampered view from the street to the arches on the second floor. I lingered until a stranger appeared at one of the windows and stared at me anxiously.

There had been three schools for boys in Sopron—my school, the Benedictine *Gymnasium*, and the Evangelical lyceum on the main square. The last two, badly damaged by bombs, had been left unrestored. I could guess that the new regime did not plan to revive ecclesiastic schools. Three hundred years old, both had taught Latin and Greek as their main subjects. My school had had a modern curriculum of French and German, as well as the sciences. In my day, the rivalry between my school and the two ecclesiastic schools was notorious, but seeing them now in their pitiable state I could feel only compassion.

I continued my walk to the Széchenyi tér, a square shaded by wild chestnut trees—our playground. On the stone benches entwined with plants we would place our jackets and books when we stopped on the way home from school to play soccer. At one side of the square was the twin-towered fifteenth-century Dominican church from which the yearly Corpus Christi procession would start, scenting the whole town with incense. One tower remained intact, but the other had been broken in half by a bomb hit. The structure looked like an invalid leaning on a cane.

Then I turned a corner, and it seemed as though I had been leading up to this moment. Often through the years —in Paris, on the Ivory Coast, in New York—during the most trying periods of my life, I had seizures of insomnia when, to calm myself, I would conjure up a tiny octagonal square and an old cloister of the Ursuline Sisters overlooking it. In the middle of the square was a spherical baroque fountain, topped by a fragile Madonna and Child standing on a serpent. That was all. Leaning on the rim of that fountain, I had waited for my first love (her name was Rózsi) to emerge from the cloister, which had housed a school for girls of "better families." Through the ornamented Gothic windows, the tinkling of the piano had sounded (better girls had to learn to play an instrument). Now the Ursuline cloister had disappeared, and so had the fountain with the Madonna. I closed my eyes, and for a moment saw it as it used to be.

I looked at my watch—in half an hour I had traversed the realm of my childhood, which once had seemed an enormous territory. There was plenty of time to visit the Jewish cemetery, on the outskirts of town. The district leading to it was that of the *Bohnzüchter*—the Bean Growers —so called because of the cranberry beans they had cultivated in the vineyards. They were well-to-do people, Germans, who had immigrated to Sopron at the time of the Reformation. They had retained their language, and in my day their sons comprised half the student body of the *Gymnasium*. As most of the Germans in lands bordering Nazi

Germany had done, they became Nazis, and at the end of the war retreated with the German armies, leaving their possessions behind. Their baroque houses were now occupied by Hungarian peasants—men wearing little round hats, and women in bright red-and-white dresses.

———————

THE cemetery was on a hill. Looking beyond the low fence that surrounded it, I could see that, unlike most Jewish cemeteries in lands occupied by the Nazis, it had not been desecrated. Nothing was changed except that the small morgue at the entrance had been replaced by a huge building—in recent years, judging by the clean whitewashed walls and the shining golden dome. Above the entrance door was an inscription: "This house was dedicated by Jewish communities of the Diaspora to our Martyrs."

The building contained only a stone bench and, on the wall opposite the entrance, a marble plaque that reached from the dome to the floor. At the summit of the plaque I read the names of the last rabbi of the community, Pollák Miksa, and his wife. Underneath, arranged alphabetically in seemingly endless columns, was name after name. I recognized the names. They were my elders, my teachers, the companions of my childhood—two thousand men, women, and children of the old Jewish community. I came to the name of my Aunt Eszti, the sister of my father, and I could read no more. I sat on the bench and wept as I had never wept in my life.

In the silence that followed, I could almost hear my heart beat. I began to think. I had prepared myself for this long before, but from thousands of miles away everything had looked different. It was good that I had come, I thought—these moments had given me a feeling of participation I had not had. But they also made me feel I must retreat, leave town as quickly as possible—slip away from the hotel and return to Vienna. The other members of the class of 1920 could celebrate without me.

———

OUTSIDE the hotel, Boross was standing with another man. He caught sight of me and rushed forward, lifting his arms in a gesture of relief. "Thank God, *doktor úr,* you're in one piece!" he exclaimed. "The principal and I began to worry."

The man I took to be Mr. Laky embraced me. "We've hunted for you all over town," he said. "Where were you hiding out?" He held me at arm's length. "But you look much younger than I expected."

He himself, in his too tight blue suit, looked not much older than a *Gymnasium* graduate—a tall, handsome man with sky-blue eyes. He peered at me. "You look tired," he said. "Too much walking. Come, let's get a bite to eat. We've not much time left."

He took my arm and led me toward the dining room. I was still numb, and made no protest. In a minute, Laky and I were seated at a table covered with a red-green-and-yellow checkered cloth. The smell of goulash pervaded the air. I was not hungry, but I felt a burning thirst. While I drank a beer, Laky asked questions about my trip and said repeatedly how happy he was to see me—until the very last he had been apprehensive that something would prevent my visit; I was, after all, a doctor. But now that I was here he and everyone in town would do their utmost to make my stay enjoyable.

As he talked on, I wondered how I could interrupt to tell him I was not staying. He talked excitedly about how

Sopron had developed since the war—from rubble. And new industries and several schools were on the drawing board. After the siege, the city had been left in a state of near extermination. The city fathers had even contemplated erasing the few structures that remained and rebuilding it. "What would you have thought, *doktor úr*," he said, "if, instead of your familiar medieval buildings, you had found skyscrapers!" He laughed heartily. But then his face turned earnest and he spoke of the new school system. The educational privileges of former middle and upper classes no longer existed. More than ninety per cent of the students were sons of peasants and workers. "In your time, how could I, the son of a coal miner at Brennbergbánya, have studied in a *Gymnasium* and at a university and become a principal? You, an old anti-Fascist, must certainly approve of what has happened—no?" He scrutinized my face for a sign of dissent and then smiled. "But we have kept what was good in the old system—the foreign-language courses, the old curriculum, the *Matura*. . . ." He looked at his wristwatch and said reluctantly, "We must go, *doktor úr*, and there is still so much to talk about."

The school was only a few blocks from the hotel, and we set off at a brisk pace. On our way we passed the former country club, a landmark of the town. Two giant red flags emblazoned with hammer and sickle flew from the eaves. It was now the House of Culture.

"Last season," said Laky, "we had the Budapest Philharmonic here. Thousands of people came for the concerts —Mozart, Beethoven, Bach, Kodály, Bartók. By the way," he asked anxiously, "do Americans appreciate Kodály and Bartók?"

My school looked dilapidated and its gray façade had lighter patches here and there where it had been repaired, but otherwise it was exactly as I knew it. I began to recall the names of my classmates—Ambrus, Becker, Böröcz,

Drobnits, Heller . . . How many would I find here? One-third of the class had been Jewish.

As we approached the school, boys and girls rushed past us, dressed in their Sunday clothes, hair combed neatly and glistening from a wetting down. They greeted their principal respectfully and looked curiously at me. It was traditional for the entire school to participate in the reunion ceremonies, but it seemed odd to see girls in these environs. In my day, the *Gymnasium* admitted boys only. "Another change for the better," Laky said when I remarked on it.

We made our way across the schoolyard framed with poplar trees. The auditorium was on the second floor, reached by a broad staircase. As we climbed, I could hear a clamor of young voices. The spacious hall was unchanged, and for a moment I felt lost in time. Would our old principal, Mr. Wallner, a man with the mustache of a grenadier, appear on the dais and harangue us about the virtues of his former students—old men sitting behind him?

The pupils sat in rows, moving restlessly and chatting. In one corner of the hall, near the door, stood the group of men I assumed to be the new generation of teachers, thirty to forty years old—mere youngsters compared with my venerable teachers. Laky took me by the arm to guide me in.

"Where are the other graduates?" I asked.

Laky stopped, looked at the floor, and then lifted his eyes sadly. "You are the only one," he said. "No one answered but you." He had written to everyone at his last known address. He had waited and waited for replies, hopeful until this last day. "I didn't dare tell you before now."

Once again he took me by the arm and led me toward the waiting group of teachers. They came forward, and suddenly all eyes in the auditorium were turned on us. There were vigorous handshakes, applause, and shouts of *"Éljen!"* ("Live long!") from a hundred young girls and boys. The solemn sounds of the national anthem, "God Bless Hungary," filled the large hall. I sang also—I had not forgotten one single word of the long text I had sung from the time I had learned to speak. Laky escorted me to the dais. A young girl with a red bow in her blond hair mounted the three steps to the dais and presented me with a large bouquet of field flowers while the music teacher played an étude of Kodály on the harmonium.

Laky stood at the rostrum, turning the pages of a manuscript. His face was flushed; he was nervous. The students, who had been standing, noisily settled in their seats. It was silent in the hall as Laky began his speech. "Comrade teachers, students, I herewith solemnly declare open the forty-fifth-anniversary reunion of the graduation class of 1920. . . ."

Hungarian orators are enthusiastic and lengthy. A speech of two hours is regarded as a short one. In his tribute to me, Laky began with the year 1912, when I entered the *Gymnasium*.

I looked down at the youngsters. I recalled how we hated these ceremonies—the reunions, the countless national holidays. I watched the young faces turn repeatedly to the sunny windows.

Laky's speech had reached the years of the revolutions after the First World War, in which, he emphasized, I had taken part as a leader of a great cause. He described as if he had witnessed it (he was born ten years after the event) how I was expelled from school. "But Richard had not lost courage," he went on. "Away from his homeland, his friends, everything that was dear to him, he started a new life—a life of great achievements. What else could have been expected of him, who in school was a paragon of scholastic excellence, and uncompromising in his fight against the dark powers of reaction? It is now my privilege to present to him the honor of which he was wrongly deprived forty-five years ago." Laky stepped down from the rostrum and embraced me. Then he presented me with a framed document—my *Matura*.

There was vigorous applause, and the ceremony was at an end. The students jumped up from the chairs and rushed from the hall into the courtyard.

<hr>

FOLLOWING the ceremony, a reception took place at the city hall, with another lengthy speech by the mayor, and that evening a banquet was tendered in my honor at the Red Star Hotel. The meal was delicious, in the best tradition of the Sopron cuisine: a thick bean soup, roast goose with red cabbage, and, of course, plenty of *kékfrankos*, a strong wine whose tradition had originated in Franconia, from where it had been brought to Sopron a half millennium before. More speeches—expressing more delight at my homecoming. Some of the speakers spoke of the improvement in relations between America and Hungary, and urged me to do my utmost to help it develop into a genuine friendship. Suddenly on the threshold of the dining room appeared Boross carrying a giant *torta*, which he placed on the table, indicating by a gesture how heavy the cake was. It was decorated with the Hungarian and American flags. The latter, I could see, was improvised. Absently I counted the stars: fifty-six altogether.

Although I was exhausted, the speeches would not end. Finally, shortly after midnight, Laky suggested that the party break up. There were disappointed faces—Hungarian affairs could go on until late afternoon of the following day. Before we separated, Laky said that at eight in the morning he would call to take me around Sopron, to show me the sights I had missed.

Boross was in a hilarious mood (after bringing in the cake, he had been invited to join the party) as he accompanied me up to my room. He took the yellow velvet cover from the bed with a grand sweep and folded it with care. He tapped his forehead as Hungarian peasants do when they think they have a good idea. "Once, an *S.S. Obergruppenführer* slept here," he said. "Later, a general of the Red Army. And now an American doctor. Good night, *doktor úr!*" He laughed with gusto.

I tossed for a long time before I fell asleep, and then my sleep was interrupted by bad dreams. In one, I found myself at the cemetery. There in the middle of the marble plaque I saw my *Matura*. I awoke; it was only three. Before long, pale daylight filtered through the curtains. At five, I got up and dressed. I took a prescription blank from my wallet and wrote a note to Laky—a few words of excuse explaining that I had miscalculated the time of my departure from Vienna. I left the note downstairs on the desk of Boross, who fortunately was still sleeping. The morning was brisk. I started my Volkswagen, and soon I was travelling on the road to the frontier.

I never again dreamed of my *Matura*.

01